HUNGARIAN PROBLEM BOOK

BASED ON THE EÖTVÖS COMPETITIONS, 1894–1905

NEW MATHEMATICAL LIBRARY

published by
Random House and The L. W. Singer Company
for the Monograph Project *of the*
SCHOOL MATHEMATICS STUDY GROUP†

EDITORIAL PANEL

† The School Mathematics Study Group represents all parts of the mathematical profession and all parts of the country. Its activities are aimed at the improvement of teaching of mathematics in our schools. Further information can be obtained from: School Mathematics Study Group, Cedar Hall, Stanford University, Stanford, California.

HUNGARIAN
PROBLEM BOOK

BASED ON THE EÖTVÖS COMPETITIONS, 1894–1905
REVISED AND EDITED BY
G. HAJÓS, G. NEUKOMM, J. SURÁNYI,
ORIGINALLY COMPILED BY JÓZSEF KÜRSCHÁK

translated by

Elvira Rapaport

Brooklyn Polytechnic Institute

11

RANDOM HOUSE
THE L. W. SINGER COMPANY

Editors' Note

The publication of distinguished problem collections in the New Mathematical Library has been one of the aims of the Monograph Project of the School Mathematics Study Group from the beginning. We are proud therefore to be able to make available to American students a translation of the Hungarian Eötvös Competition Problems from 1894–1928,† based on the revised Hungarian edition of József Kürschák's original compilation of problems and solutions. This revised edition, published in 1955, was edited by Professors Hajós, Neukomm and Surányi.

We are grateful to Professors Hajós and Surányi‡ for their help in preparing this translation. While we made every effort to preserve the spirit of the Hungarian problem collection, some minor changes were necessary in the American edition because of the differences between the mathematical background of American high school students and that of their Hungarian counterparts; these consist of occasional additions to the solutions and to the explanatory notes, occasional abbreviations, and a few small changes in proofs.

To conform to the design of the New Mathematical Library, we had to publish the contest problems from 1894–1928 in two volumes. If these turn out to be as useful as we hope, we shall probably publish the problems from 1929 to date as well.

The reader should be aware that this collection is far from routine. While the solutions require elementary mathematical techniques only, a great deal of ingenuity is often necessary. The main purpose of this collection is to instruct the reader by having him study the solutions presented here together with some of the more sophisticated material in the explanatory notes. The reader should not feel that he is being tested, but that he is being taught.

We gratefully acknowledge the excellent work of the translator, Dr. Elvira Rapaport, the invaluable advice of Professors Pólya and Szegő, and the suggestions made by those familiar with the American school curriculum, in particular by Mr. H. C. Wolfson of Bushwick High School, New York City.

The Editors

New York, 1962

† Problems from 1894–1905 are contained in the present volume, those from 1906–1928 appear in the NML companion volume.
‡ Professor Neukomm died in 1957.

NEW MATHEMATICAL LIBRARY

Other titles will be announced when ready

CONTENTS

HUNGARIAN PROBLEM BOOK

BASED ON THE EÖTVÖS COMPETITIONS, 1894–1905

From the Hungarian Prefaces

The first of these contests was held in 1894 by the Mathematical and Physical Society (of Hungary) in honor of its founder and president, the distinguished physicist Baron Loránd Eötvös, who became minister of education that year. To commemorate the event, the contests are given every fall and are open to high school graduates of that year. The contestants work in classrooms under supervision; the Society selects the two best papers, and the awards—a first and second Eötvös Prize—are given to the winners by the president himself at the next session of the Society.

The present volume, appearing on the tenth anniversary of Eötvös' death, contains the contests held to date. While it utilizes the winners' work, the solutions are in general not those found by the students . . . .

The names of the winners are listed; their papers appeared in full in *Matematikai és Fizikai Lapok*, the Journal of the Society; here, however, the solutions were changed to suit the didactic aim of the book.

Some of my notes give definitions and proofs of theorems used in the solutions. Others serve to point out the connection between problems and famous results in literature. In some instances I was able to give a glimpse of the essence of an entire subject matter; in others the mere statement of a general theorem had to suffice . . . .

There are few prerequisites. A person who has learned to solve quadratic equations and knows plane geometry can solve many of the problems. If he also knows trigonometry, he can solve most of them. So little of the material taught in the last two years of high school (in Hungary) is needed here that a younger student can easily learn it from books.

However, this book is meant not only for students and teachers. Anyone who retained an interest in mathematics in his adult life can find things of note and value here and will be gratified to see how much can be achieved with the elementary material to which high schools must restrict themselves.

How should the reader use this book? All I can say is: without frenzy. With a serious interest and perseverence, everyone will find the way best suited *to him* in order to benefit from the varied material contained in it . . . .

József Kürschák

Budapest, April 9th, 1929

Problems of the Mathematics Contests, edited by József Kürschák, was published originally in 1929. The first edition was quickly sold out and the Ministry of Education commissioned a new edition. We are undertaking this work with pleasure and in the hope of contributing to the attainment of Kürschák's goal. This volume will soon be followed by another containing a similar treatment of the contests held since.

The new edition required certain changes. By and large, Kürschák's approach was retained, especially his notes which were meant to widen the reader's horizon. We augmented these notes here and there, changing them only to conform to present-day high school curricula. For example, we added permutations, the binomial theorem, half-angle formulas, etc. We added a few new notes. We included some new solutions that seemed strikingly simple or ingenious, and so we deviated from the contestants' work more than the first edition did . . . .

We made a few technical changes to facilitate handling. Thus, we repeated the problems before giving the solution and we unified the notation, thereby necessitating alterations in and additions to the figures . . . .

We sincerely hope to have come up to expectation and that this work will give pleasure and profit to many.

György Hajós
Gyula Neukomm
János Surányi

Budapest, September, 1955

Preface to the American Edition

In recent times much effort has been devoted to the improvement of mathematics teaching on all levels. Thus it is only natural that we search for further stimulants and improvements in this direction, as well as for new means of discovering and developing the dormant abilities which may exist in our society. The Monograph Project of the School Mathematics Study Group has such a purpose. The present translation of the Hungarian problem collection of the Eötvös Competition serves this goal. Since I am one of the few still existing links between the present mathematical generation and an older one that witnessed the first phase of the interesting development of this competition, I was asked to write a few introductory words to the English version of this collection.

The Eötvös Competition was organized in Hungary in 1894 and played a remarkable role in the development of mathematics in that small country.† The competition was open to all freshmen entering the university; the publication of the problems and the names of the winners was from the beginning a public event of first class interest. Among the winners during the period of the first decade of the competition were such men as Fejér, von Kármán, Haar, Riesz, and numerous others who later became internationally known. With some short interruptions due to wars and related conditions the competition has been carried on to the present day, though the name was changed, and the organization and scope of the competition have become much broader in recent years. The essence however has remained the same. The problems are almost all

† Before the first world war Hungary had 19 million inhabitants; at present it has about 10 million.

from high school material (no calculus is included), they are of an elementary character, but rather difficult, and their solution requires a certain degree of insight and creative ability. Any amount of aid in the form of books or notes is permitted.

Mathematics is a human activity almost as diverse as the human mind itself. Therefore it seems impossible to design absolutely certain and effective means and methods for the stimulation of mathematics on a large scale. While the competitive idea seems to be a powerful stimulant, it is interesting to observe that it was and is still almost completely absent from academic life in Germany although mathematics has flourished in that country throughout the last two hundred years. The organization of the Eötvös Competition in Hungary was probably suggested by British and French examples that had existed in those countries for a long time. We mention in particular the "Mathematical Tripos" in Cambridge, England and the "Concours" examination problems for admission to the "Grandes Écoles" in France. These early examples suggest also that some sort of preparation is essential to arouse public interest, to attract the best competitors and to give them proper recognition. In England the participation in the Tripos is preceded by systematic coaching, and in France the public schools offer facilities to prepare for the "Concours" examinations. In Hungary a similar objective was achieved by a Journal published primarily for high school students as another natural stimulant to the student's preparation for participation in the competition upon entering the university.†

The Journal was organized almost simultaneously with the competition, i.e. in 1894, by Dániel Arany; for many years it was edited by the able high school teacher László Rácz‡ and later by various other teachers of high quality. The articles were supplied partly by teachers and partly by mathematicians affiliated with the university, mostly younger persons. The Journal carried articles primarily from elementary mathematics, much triangle geometry, some projective and descriptive geometry, algebra and occasionally some number theory, later also some ventures into calculus. But the most important and most fertile part was the

---

† A good account of the Eötvös Competition and of the Journal is given in an article by Tibor Radó: "On mathematical life in Hungary", *American Mathematical Monthly*, vol. 39 (1932), pp. 85–90. (One slight correction has to be made on p. 87, line 6: There *was* a girl winner, first prize, 1908.)

‡ His name will go down in history for a second reason: Rácz was the teacher of J. von Neumann in high school. Cf. the Obituary Note by S. Ulam, *Bulletin of the American Mathematical Society*, vol. 64 (1958), pp. 1–49; on p. 2 the name Rácz appears in distorted spelling.

problem section; it occupied a large part of the content and was essentially written for the students and by the students. The best solution sent in was printed with the name and school of the author, and a list of the others who sent in correct solutions was given.

I remember vividly the time when I participated in this phase of the Journal (in the years between 1908 and 1912); I would wait eagerly for the arrival of the monthly issue and my first concern was to look at the problem section, almost breathlessly, and to start grappling with the problems without delay. The names of the others who were in the same business were quickly known to me and frequently I read with considerable envy how they had succeeded with some problems which I could not handle with complete success, or how they had found a better solution (that is, simpler, more elegant or wittier) than the one I had sent in. The following story may not be accurate in all details but it is certainly revealing:

"The time is about 1940, the scene is one of the infamous labor camps of fascist Hungary just at the beginning of its pathetic transformation from semi-dictatorship to the cannibalism of the Nazi pattern. These camps were populated mostly by Jewish youth forced to carry out some perfectly useless tasks. One young man (at present one of the leading mathematicians of Hungary) was in the camp; let us call him Mr. X. He was panting under the load of a heavy beam when the sergeant shouted at him in a not too complimentary manner, addressing him by his last name. The supervising officer stood nearby, just a few steps away, and said: 'Say, did I hear right, your name is X?' 'Yes,' was the answer. 'Are you by chance the same X who worked years ago in the High School Journal?' 'Yes,' was again the answer. 'You know, you solved more, and more difficult problems than any one of us and we were very envious of you.' The end of the story is that Mr. X received more lenient treatment in the camp and later even had some mathematical contact with the all-powerful officer."

The profound interest which these young men took in the Journal was decisive in many of their lives. The intensive preoccupation with interesting problems of simple and elementary character and the effort of finding clear and complete answers gave them a new experience, the taste of creative intellectual adventure. Thus they were bound finally and unalterably to the jealous mistress that mathematics is. There remained still the question of what special studies to undertake, whether it should be mathematics or physics or engineering; but this was after all a secondary matter; the main road was charted for life. We may think of the adage of Kronecker who compares mathematicians with lotus eaters: "Wer einmal von dieser Kost etwas zu sich genommen hat, kann nie mehr davon lassen." (He who has once tasted of this fruit can never more forswear it.)

And a final observation. We should not forget that the solution of any worth-while problem very rarely comes to us easily and without hard work; it is rather the result of intellectual effort of days or weeks or months. Why should the young mind be willing to make this supreme effort? The explanation is probably the instinctive preference for certain values, that is, the attitude which rates intellectual effort and spiritual achievement higher than material advantage. Such a valuation can only be the result of a long cultural development of environment and public spirit which is difficult to accelerate by governmental aid or even by more intensive training in mathematics. The most effective means may consist of transmitting to the young mind the beauty of intellectual work and the feeling of satisfaction following a great and successful mental effort. The hope is justified that the present book might aid exactly in this respect and that it represents a good step in the right direction.

Gábor Szegő

Stanford University, February, 1961

Problems

1894 Competition

1894/1. Prove that the expressions

$$2x + 3y \quad \text{and} \quad 9x + 5y$$

are divisible by 17 for the same set of integral values of x and y.

1894/2. Given a circle and two points, P and Q: construct an inscribed right triangle such that one of its legs goes through the given point P and the other through the given point Q. For what position of the points P and Q is this construction impossible?

1894/3. The lengths of the sides of a triangle form an arithmetic progression with difference d. The area of the triangle is t. Find the sides and angles of this triangle. Solve this problem for the case $d = 1$ and $t = 6$.

1895 Competition

1895/1. Prove that there are $2(2^{n-1} - 1)$ ways of dealing n cards to two persons. (The players may receive unequal numbers of cards.)

1895/2. Given a right triangle ABC, construct a point N inside the triangle such that the angles NBC, NCA and NAB are equal.

9

1895/3. Given the following information about a triangle: the radius R of its circumscribed circle, the length c of one of its sides, and the ratio a/b of the lengths of the other two sides; determine all three sides and angles of this triangle.

1896 Competition

1896/1. Prove that

$$\log n \geq k \cdot \log 2,$$

where n is a natural number and k the number of distinct primes that divide n.

1896/2. Prove that the equations

$$x^2 - 3xy + 2y^2 + x - y = 0$$

and

$$x^2 - 2xy + y^2 - 5x + 7y = 0$$

imply the equation

$$xy - 12x + 15y = 0.$$

1896/3. Construct a triangle, given the feet of its altitudes. Express the lengths of the sides of the solution triangle Y in terms of the lengths of the sides of the triangle X whose vertices are the feet of the altitudes of triangle Y.

1897 Competition

1897/1. Prove, for the angles α, β and γ of a right triangle, the following relation:

$$\sin \alpha \sin \beta \sin(\alpha-\beta) + \sin \beta \sin \gamma \sin(\beta-\gamma) + \sin \gamma \sin \alpha \sin(\gamma-\alpha)$$

$$+ \sin (\alpha - \beta) \sin (\beta - \gamma) \sin (\gamma - \alpha) = 0.$$

1897/2. Show that, if α, β and γ are angles of an arbitrary triangle, then

$$\sin \frac{\alpha}{2} \sin \frac{\beta}{2} \sin \frac{\gamma}{2} < \frac{1}{4}.$$

1897/3. Let $ABCD$ be a rectangle and let M, N and P, Q be the points of intersection of some line e with the sides AB, CD and AD, BC, respectively (or their extensions). Given the points M, N, P, Q and the length p of the side AB, construct the rectangle. Under what conditions can this problem be solved, and how many solutions does it have?

1898 Competition

1898/1. Determine all positive integers n for which $2^n + 1$ is divisible by 3.

1898/2. Prove the following theorem: If two triangles have a common angle, then the sum of the sines of the angles will be larger in that triangle where the difference of the remaining two angles is smaller.

On the basis of this theorem, determine the shape of that triangle for which the sum of the sines of its angles is a maximum.

1898/3. Let A, B, C, D be four given points on a straight line e. Construct a square such that two of its parallel sides (or their extensions) go through A and B respectively, and the other two sides (or their extensions) go through C and D, respectively.

1899 Competition

1899/1. The points A_0, A_1, A_2, A_3, A_4 divide a unit circle (circle of radius 1) into five equal parts. Prove that the chords A_0A_1, A_0A_2 satisfy $(A_0A_1 \cdot A_0A_2)^2 = 5$.

1899/2. Let x_1 and x_2 be the roots of the equation

$$x^2 - (a + d)x + ad - bc = 0.$$

Show that x_1^3 and x_2^3 are the roots of

$$y^2 - (a^3 + d^3 + 3abc + 3bcd)y + (ad - bc)^3 = 0.$$

1899/3. Prove that, for any natural number n, the expression

$$A = 2903^n - 803^n - 464^n + 261^n$$

is divisible by 1897.

1900 Competition

1900/1. Let a, b, c, d be fixed integers with d not divisible by 5. Assume that m is an integer for which

$$am^3 + bm^2 + cm + d$$

is divisible by 5. Prove that there exists an integer n for which

$$dn^3 + cn^2 + bn + a$$

is also divisible by 5.

1900/2. Construct a triangle ABC, given the length c of its side AB, the radius r of its inscribed circle, and the radius r_c of its ex-circle tangent to the side AB and to the extensions of BC and CA.

1900/3. A cliff is 300 meters high. Consider two free-falling raindrops such that the second one leaves the top of the cliff when the first one has already fallen 0.001 millimeters. What is the distance between the drops at the moment the first hits the ground? (Compute the answer to within 0.1 mm. Neglect air resistance, etc.)

1901 Competition

1901/1. Prove that, for any positive integer n,

$$1^n + 2^n + 3^n + 4^n$$

is divisible by 5 if and only if n is not divisible by 4.

1901/2. If

$$u = \cot 22°30', \qquad v = \frac{1}{\sin 22°30'},$$

prove that u satisfies a quadratic and v a quartic (4th degree) equation with integral coefficients and with leading coefficients 1.

1901/3. Let a and b be two natural numbers whose greatest common divisor (g.c.d.) is d. Prove that exactly d of the numbers

$$a, \quad 2a, \quad 3a, \quad \cdots, \quad (b-1)a, \quad ba$$

are divisible by b.

1902 Competition

1902/1. Prove that any quadratic expression

$$Q(x) = Ax^2 + Bx + C$$

a) can be put uniquely into the form

$$Q(x) = k\frac{x(x-1)}{1 \cdot 2} + lx + m,$$

where k, l, m depend on the coefficients A, B, C, and

b) $Q(x)$ takes on integral values for every integer x if and only if k, l, m are integers.

1902/2. Let S be a given sphere with center O and radius r. Let P be any point outside the sphere S, and let S' be the sphere with center P and radius PO. Denote by F the area of the surface of the part of S' that lies inside S. Prove that F is independent of the particular point P chosen.

1902/3. The area T and an angle γ of a triangle are given. Determine the lengths of the sides a and b so that the side c, opposite the angle γ, is as short as possible.

1903 Competition

1903/1. Let $n = 2^{p-1}(2^p - 1)$, and let $2^p - 1$ be a prime number. Prove that the sum of all (positive) divisors of n (not including n itself) is exactly n.

1903/2. For a given pair of values x and y satisfying $x = \sin \alpha$, $y = \sin \beta$, there can be four different values of $z = \sin (\alpha + \beta)$.

a) Set up a relation between x, y and z not involving trigonometric functions or radicals.

b) Find those pairs of values (x, y) for which $z = \sin (\alpha + \beta)$ takes on fewer than four distinct values.

1903/3. Let A, B, C, D be the vertices of a rhombus; let k_1 be the circle through $B, C,$ and D; let k_2 be the circle through $A, C,$ and D; let

k_3 be the circle through A, B, and D; and let k_4 be the circle through A, B, and C. Prove that the tangents to k_1 and k_3 at B form the same angle as the tangents to k_2 and k_4 at A.

1904 Competition

1904/1. Prove that, if a pentagon (five-sided polygon) inscribed in a circle has equal angles, then its sides are equal.

1904/2. If a is a natural number, show that the number of positive integral solutions of the indeterminate equation

$$(1) \qquad x_1 + 2x_2 + 3x_3 + \cdots + nx_n = a$$

is equal to the number of non-negative integral solutions of

$$(2) \qquad y_1 + 2y_2 + 3y_3 + \cdots + ny_n = a - \frac{n(n+1)}{2}.$$

[By a *solution* of equation (1), we mean a set of numbers $\{x_1, x_2, \cdots, x_n\}$ which satisfies equation (1).]

1904/3. Let A_1A_2 and B_1B_2 be the diagonals of a rectangle, and let O be its center. Find and construct the set of all points P that satisfy simultaneously the four inequalities

$$A_1P > OP, \quad A_2P > OP, \quad B_1P > OP, \quad B_2P > OP.$$

1905 Competition

1905/1. For given positive integers n and p, find necessary and sufficient conditions for the system of equations

$$x + py = n, \qquad x + y = p^z$$

to have a solution (x, y, z) of positive integers. Prove also that there is at most one such solution.

1905/2. Divide the unit square into 9 equal squares by means of two pairs of lines parallel to the sides (see Figure 38). Now remove the central square. Treat the remaining 8 squares the same way, and repeat the process n times.

a) How many squares of side length $1/3^n$ remain?
b) What is the sum of the areas of the removed squares as n becomes infinite?

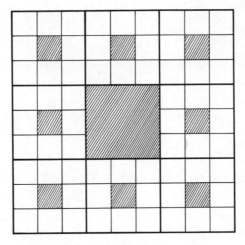

Figure 38

1905/3. Let C_1 be any point on side AB of a triangle ABC (see Figure 39), and draw C_1C. Let A_1 be the intersection of BC extended and the line through A parallel to CC_1; similarly let B_1 be the intersection of AC extended and the line through B parallel to CC_1. Prove that

$$\frac{1}{AA_1} + \frac{1}{BB_1} = \frac{1}{CC_1}.$$

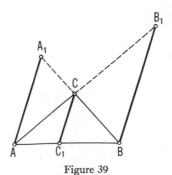

Figure 39

Solutions

1894/1. Prove that the expressions

$$2x + 3y \quad \text{and} \quad 9x + 5y$$

are divisible by 17 for the same set of integral values of x and y.

First Solution. a) First let us determine those integral values of x and y for which the expression $2x + 3y$ is equal to some given integer k.

From the equation

(1) $$2x + 3y = k$$

we obtain

(2) $$x = \frac{k - 3y}{2} = -y + \frac{k - y}{2}.$$

From (2) we see that x is an integer only if $(k - y)/2$ is an integer, say $(k - y)/2 = s$. Hence

$$y = k - 2s$$

and (2) yields

$$x = -y + s = -(k - 2s) + s = 3s - k.$$

Therefore, if the integers x and y satisfy equation (1), they are necessarily of the form

(3) $$x = -k + 3s, \quad y = k - 2s$$

where s is some integer. Conversely, for an arbitrary integer s, (3) defines integers x and y, which satisfy equation (1).

17

b) In a similar manner we can determine the integral solutions of

(4) $9x + 5y = l.$

where l is a given integer. From (4) we obtain

(5) $y = \dfrac{l - 9x}{5} = -2x + \dfrac{l + x}{5}.$

From (5) we see that y is an integer only if $(l + x)/5$ is an integer, say

$$\frac{l + x}{5} = t.$$

Hence

$$x = 5t - l$$

and, substituting in (5),

$$y = -2x + t = -2(5t - l) + t = -9t + 2l.$$

Therefore, if the integers x and y satisfy equation (4), they are necessarily of the form

(6) $x = 5t - l, \qquad y = -9t + 2l,$

where t is an integer. Conversely, for an arbitrary integer t, (6) defines integers x and y which satisfy equation (4).

c) If $2x + 3y$ is equal to some multiple of 17, say $17 \cdot n$, then according to a),

$$x = -17n + 3s,$$

$$y = 17n - 2s.$$

(Here n and s are, of course, integers.) Then

$$9x + 5y = 9(-17n + 3s) + 5(17n - 2s)$$

$$= 17(-4n + s);$$

that is, if $2x + 3y$ is divisible by 17, then so is $9x + 5y$. Using the result of b), we can see in an analogous manner that for all integers x and y for which $9x + 5y$ is divisible by 17, $2x + 3y$ is also divisible by 17.

Note. Divisibility. Classification of the integers. *Definition*: We say that the integer b divides the integer a if there exists an integer k such that k times b is equal to a. In this case we also say that a is a multiple of b, or b is a divisor of a.

The integers a, b, and k need not be positive. Any of them might be negative, and a and k might be zero.

If a is divisible by b and b is divisible by c then a is divisible by c.

If a and a' are divisible by b then so is $a + a'$ and $a - a'$. If b is a divisor of the integer a and if a is different from zero, then the absolute value of b is not greater than the absolute value of a. Thus a number different from zero has only a finite number of different divisors. For example, the divisors of 12 are ± 1, ± 2, ± 3, ± 4, ± 6, ± 12.

In enumerating the divisors of a number, we shall restrict outselves to the positive ones; the negative divisors can be obtained by simply changing the sign. (Zero cannot be a divisor of any integer.)

The only positive divisor of the positive and negative units (i.e. of $+1$ and -1) is 1.

Every integer whose absolute value is greater than 1 has at least two positive divisors: its absolute value and 1.

If an integer p whose absolute value is greater than 1 has no other positive divisor except $|p|$ and 1, then p is called a *prime number*.

If an integer a whose absolute value is greater than 1 has a positive divisor, say b, different from $|a|$ and 1, then a can be written in the form

$$a = kb.$$

Here not only b but also $|k|$ is between 1 and $|a|$. Hence a can be written as a product of two numbers whose absolute values are greater than 1 and less than $|a|$. Such an integer a is called a *composite number*.

Zero is divisible by every integer.

We can now divide the integers into four different classes as follows:

the positive and negative units

the prime numbers

the composite numbers

zero.

The study of the divisibility properties of integers belongs to number theory. A detailed discussion of its foundation can be found in *Euclid's Elements, Books VIII–IX*.†

† The Greek mathematician Euclid lived in Alexandria around 300 B.C. His most important work, the *Elements*, is a systematic and unified presentation of the mathematics known in his time. It contains plane and solid geometry, number theory, the theory of proportions, and the solution of second degree equations. This work is often considered the pinnacle of rigorous logical thinking. Thus, Spinoza (Dutch philosopher, 1632–1677) wrote in his ethics "more geometrico demonstrata".

Second Solution. For the sake of brevity let

$$u = 2x + 3y, \qquad v = 9x + 5y.$$

Hence

$$3v - 5u = 17x.$$

This can be written in the following two ways:

(1) $$3v = 5u + 17x,$$

(2) $$5u = 3v - 17x.$$

If x and y are integers such that u is divisible by 17, then from (1) $3v$ is also divisible by 17. Since the first factor, 3, of the product $3v$ is not divisible by 17, the above implies that v is divisible by 17.

Using equation (2), we can see in a similar manner that if the integers x and y are such that v is divisible by 17, then so is u.

Note. An important property of prime numbers. The second solution of our problem is based on the following property of prime numbers:

a) *If neither of two numbers is divisible by a given prime number p, then their product is not divisible by p.*

It is sufficient to consider natural numbers; for, on the one hand, any number has the same divisors as its negative, and on the other hand, the negative divisors of a number are -1 times the positive divisors of that number.

We shall verify the following equivalent form of the statement to be proved:

If a natural number a is not divisible by a prime p then ab is divisible by p only if b is.

Given a prime p and a number a not divisible by p; denote by B the set of those natural numbers b for which ab is divisible by p. (p and all its multiples clearly belong to B.) Let us find the smallest number in B. Such a number exists; to find it we merely have to decide which of the numbers

(1) $$a \cdot 1, \quad a \cdot 2 \ \cdots, \quad a(p-1), \quad a \cdot p$$

is divisible by p. Surely $a \cdot p$ is divisible by p. If, in the sequence (1), $a \cdot m$ is the first number divisible by p, then m is the smallest number in B.

We shall show on the one hand that *every number in B is divisible by m* and, on the other hand, that *m is equal to p.*

Assume to the contrary that some element b in B is not divisible by m. Let $m \cdot q$ be the largest multiple of m not exceeding b, that is

$$b = m \cdot q + r,$$

where the remainder r is one of the numbers 1, 2, $\cdots$, $m-1$. We shall show that r belongs to B, which is impossible. Multiply the above equality by a. Then

$$ab = amq + ar$$

or

$$ar = ab - (am)q.$$

The first term on the right is divisible by p and so is the second, since the factor in parenthesis is divisible by p. Thus ar is divisible by p, i.e. r is in B. But this is impossible since $0 < r < m$ and m was the smallest number such that its product by a is divisible by p. This contradiction shows that our assumption was incorrect; thus b must be divisible by m.

We know that p belongs to B and therefore, according to the statement just proved, also p is divisible by m. But the only divisors of p are 1 and p; m cannot be 1 because we have assumed that $a \cdot 1 = a$ is not divisible by p. Therefore, m must be equal to p. This proves our second assertion and thus the proof of theorem a) is complete.

Theorem a) can be generalized as follows:

b) *If none of the numbers*

$$a, \quad b, \quad c, \quad d, \quad \cdots$$

is divisible by p, then the products

$$ab, \quad abc = (ab)c, \quad abcd = (abc)d, \quad \cdots$$

are not divisible by p.

c) The following simple proposition is often useful:
A set A of positive integers contains a smallest number.
We have proved and applied this principle to the set B in the above proof of theorem a). The same proof applies to the general case: Let a be any element of A; then it is sufficient to find, among the numbers 1, 2, $\cdots$, $a-1, a$, the smallest belonging to A. This will be the smallest element of A.

It is essential that we are dealing here with positive integers. For instance, among all even integers (not necessarily positive), or among the reciprocals of all natural numbers (the set of reciprocals contains only one integer) there is no smallest.

1894/2. Given a circle and two points, P and Q; construct an inscribed right triangle such that one of its legs goes through the given point P and the other through the given point Q. For what position of the points P and Q is this construction impossible?

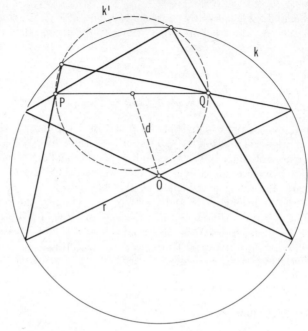

Figure 1

Solution. The locus of points P' for which angle $PP'Q$ is a right angle is a circle k' with diameter PQ; see Figure 1. The points of intersection of this circle with the given circle k are the (right-angle) vertices of those inscribed right triangles whose legs, or their continuations, go through the points P and Q. In order that P and Q lie on the legs themselves (as required by the problem), P and Q must be inside the circle k. In this case, the problem has as many solutions as the circles k and k' have points in common. Thus, if r denotes the radius of k, and d the distance from the center of k to the midpoint of the segment PQ, the problem has

    1. two solutions if $\frac{1}{2}PQ > r - d$,

    2. one solution if $\frac{1}{2}PQ = r - d$,

    3. no solution if $\frac{1}{2}PQ < r - d$,

because the shortest distance from k to k' is exactly $r - d$.

1894/3. The lengths of the sides of a triangle form an arithmetic progression with difference d. The area of the triangle is t. Find the sides and angles of this triangle. Solve this problem for the case $d = 1$ and $t = 6$.

Solution. The sides a, b, c of the triangle may be represented by

$$a = b - d, \quad b, \quad c = b + d,$$

where $0 < d < b$. We use Heron's formula†

$$t^2 = s(s - a)(s - b)(s - c)$$

where

$$s = \frac{a + b + c}{2}.$$

In the present case,

$$s = \frac{3b}{2}, \quad s - a = \frac{b}{2} + d, \quad s - b = \frac{b}{2}, \quad s - c = \frac{b}{2} - d.$$

By inserting these values in the above formula, we obtain

$$t^2 = \frac{3b^2}{4}\left(\frac{b^2}{4} - d^2\right)$$

or

$$3(b^2)^2 - 12d^2b^2 - 16t^2 = 0.$$

This is a quadratic equation in b^2 and may be solved for b^2 in terms of d and t:

$$b^2 = 2(d^2 \pm \sqrt{d^4 + 4t^2/3}\,).$$

In order to obtain a positive value for b^2, it is necessary to take the positive square root; hence

$$b = \sqrt{2(d^2 + \sqrt{d^4 + 4t^2/3})}, \quad a = b - d, \quad c = b + d.$$

The angles α and β, opposite the sides a and b, are necessarily acute: they can be calculated from the formulas

$$t = \frac{bc \sin \alpha}{2}, \quad t = \frac{ac \sin \beta}{2};$$

$$\sin \alpha = \frac{2t}{bc}, \quad \sin \beta = \frac{2t}{ac}.$$

Finally, $\gamma = 180° - (\alpha + \beta)$.

---

† For a simple derivation, see e.g. N. D. Kazarinoff, *Geometric Inequalities*, Chapter 2, pages 35, 36, in this series.

If $d = 1$ and $t = 6$, then from the above formula, $b = 4$; therefore $a = 3$ and $c = 5$. Moreover,

$$\sin \alpha = \frac{12}{20} = \frac{3}{5}, \qquad \sin \beta = \frac{4}{5} = \cos \alpha,$$

so that

$$\alpha = 36°52', \quad \beta = 90° - \alpha = 53°8', \quad \gamma = 90°.$$

1895 Competition

1895/1. Prove that there are $2(2^{n-1} - 1)$ ways of dealing n cards to two persons. (The players may receive unequal numbers of cards.)

Solution. Let us number the cards and, for the moment only, admit the two cases that all cards go to one of the players. With two cards we can then have the deals

(1) $\qquad\qquad AA, \quad AB, \quad BA, \quad BB,$

where, for example, BA means that B gets card 1, A gets card 2.

With three cards there are $2 \cdot 4 = 8$ possibilities:

$$AAA \quad ABA \quad BAA \quad BBA$$

$$AAB \quad ABB \quad BAB \quad BBB,$$

where, for example, BAB means that B receives card 1, A receives card 2, B gets card 3. The first row here is (1) with A attached and the second is (1) with B attached to each entry.

Every additional card doubles the number of possibilities. Hence for n cards there are 2^n deals; they may be called permutations of two things, A and B, n at a time, with repetitions allowed.

If no player may hold all the cards, there are $2^n - 2 = 2(2^{n-1} - 1)$ possibilities, as was to be proved. The excluded cases are the permutations containing either only A-symbols or B-symbols.

If we indicate the above permutations with the numbers 1 and 2 in place of A and B, we obtain the following theorem:

THEOREM. *There exist $2^n - 2$ numbers that have n digits made up only of the numbers 1 and 2 and contain each at least once.*

Note 1. Permutations with repetitions. Our theorem is in effect a special case ($n = 2$) of the following:

There are m^n permutations of m things, n at a time, with repetitions allowed.

It may be of interest, though beyond the scope of our problem, to discuss such permutations here.

To find all permutations of m things, n at a time, we mark n places, ordered as first place, second place, and so on, to be filled with the given elements every possible way. If *repetition is allowed*, we can use each element repeatedly. We imagine these places *in a horizontal row*. This is *not* essential, for we could choose, say, the *vertices of a regular n-gon inscribed in a circle* and numbered consecutively clockwise or counter-clockwise. If we did this, we could rotate the labels of the elements about the center of the circle, keeping the vertices fixed; if the rotation is $360°/n$ and in a direction counter to the numbering of the places, we call the resulting permutation a *cyclic permutation* of the original. For example, in Figures 2–4 the second arrangement is a cyclic permutation of the first, the third of the second. One more cyclic permutation would bring us back to the original one.[†] Cyclic permutations are characterized by the fact that the place of every element is occupied by its right-hand neighbor, the place of the last element by the first. If a combination V is obtained from another, U, by cyclic permutations, then U can be obtained from V likewise, so that they are *obtained from each other* by cyclic permutations.

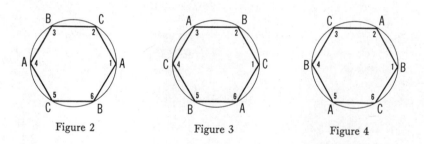

Figure 2   Figure 3   Figure 4

If V is obtained from U by k cyclic permutations, and W from V by l such, then W is obtained from U by $k + l$ cyclic permutations.

All this is clear if we view cyclic permutations as rotations. Let us classify permutations (n things at a time, repetitions allowed): *A set shall contain those, and only those, permutations which can be obtained from each other by cyclic permutations. Then the number of permutations in any such set divides the number n.*

To show this, let U_0 be a permutation in a given set. Each of its members is one of the permutations

$$(1) \qquad U_0, \quad U_1, \quad \cdots, \quad U_r, \quad \cdots, \quad U_s, \quad \cdots,$$

where U_r is obtained from U_0 by r cyclic permutations, and each permutation in (1) belongs to the class under consideration. We have only to decide how many of the permutations in (1) are *distinct*.

† In the usual notation, these permutations are: $ACBACB, CBACBA, BACBAC$.

If U_r and U_s are equal, then U_{r+1} and U_{s+1} are also equal; if U_r and U_s are distinct, so are U_{r+1} and U_{s+1}. Let U_s stand for the *first* permutation in (1) that is equal to a previous one, say to U_r. Then $r = 0$; otherwise U_{s-1} would already equal U_{r-1}. The combinations

$$U_0, \quad U_1, \quad \cdots, \quad U_{s-1}$$

simply repeat in (1). Hence the class in question consists of just these s permutations.

Only the permutations

$$U_0, \quad U_s, \quad U_{2s}, \quad \cdots$$

in (1) are all equal to U_0. Clearly U_n is also equal to U_0. It follows that the number n is equal to one of the numbers $s, 2s, 3s, \cdots$, so that s indeed divides n.†

Note 2. Combinations. a) The problem can be attacked in yet another way: We must deal 1, 2, 3, $\cdots$, $n - 2$, or $n - 1$ cards to A, and give the rest to B. If A gets k cards ($k = 1, \cdots, n - 1$), it is immaterial in what order he receives them (we may even hand out several cards at a time); two deals are the same if and only if A's holdings are identical.

Thus the question is: *In how many ways can one pick k elements (cards) from among n distinct elements regardless of the order in which they were chosen.* The sets chosen are called *combinations of n things, k at a time*; the number of possibilities is written

$$\binom{n}{k} \text{ (in words: } n \text{ over } k)$$

and is sometimes called *binomial coefficient*. (See Note 2 to 1902/1.)

In terms of these symbols, the number of possibilities is

$$\binom{n}{1} + \binom{n}{2} + \cdots + \binom{n}{n-2} + \binom{n}{n-1}.$$

This result is useful only if we can find a simple way to compute the binomial coefficients.

b) To determine the number of distinct possible combinations, let us see how to produce all combinations of n things, k at a time, if we already have them for $k - 1$ at a time where $k > 1$. We can add to a given combination

† These considerations date back to Gauss, who treated the case where n is prime. K. F. Gauss, *princeps mathematicorum* (prince of mathematicians), noted physicist and astronomer, was born in 1777 in Braunschweig and died in 1855 in Göttingen, where he taught from 1807 at the university and was director of the observatory. His epochmaking number-theoretical work, the *Disquisitiones arithmeticae*, appeared in Leipzig in 1801. His statue, in his home town, stands on a pedestal having the shape of a regular 17-gon to signify that he invented the method for constructing the regular 17-gon by ruler and compass.

of $k - 1$ objects any one of the remaining $n - k + 1$ objects, and this seems to give us

$$(n - k + 1) \cdot \binom{n}{k - 1}$$

possibilities for a tentative answer. But in this number each combination of n things, k at a time, has been counted k times. The reason for this is that every member of a collection of k objects can be the "added" object.

This shows that the following products are equal:

$$(n - k + 1) \binom{n}{k - 1} = k \binom{n}{k},$$

i.e.,

(2)
$$\binom{n}{k} = \frac{n - k + 1}{k} \binom{n}{k - 1}.$$

Obviously,

$$\binom{n}{1} = n.$$

This and (2) give:

$$\binom{n}{2} = \frac{n - 1}{2} \binom{n}{1} = \frac{n(n - 1)}{1 \cdot 2}, \qquad \binom{n}{3} = \frac{n - 2}{3} \binom{n}{2} = \frac{n(n - 1)(n - 2)}{1 \cdot 2 \cdot 3},$$

$$\binom{n}{4} = \frac{n - 3}{4} \binom{n}{3} = \frac{n(n - 1)(n - 2)(n - 3)}{1 \cdot 2 \cdot 3 \cdot 4}, \qquad \text{etc.}$$

Continuing this way, with $k = 1, 2, \cdots, n$, we get

(3)
$$\binom{n}{k} = \frac{n(n - 1) \cdots (n - k + 1)}{1 \cdot 2 \cdot 3 \cdot \cdots \cdot k}.$$

c) The product $1 \cdot 2 \cdot 3 \cdot \cdots \cdot k$ is usually denoted by $k!$ and called "k factorial". If we multiply numerator and denominator in (3) by

$$(n - k)! = (n - k)(n - k - 1) \cdot \cdots \cdot 3 \cdot 2 \cdot 1,$$

then the binomial coefficient appears in a new form:

(4)
$$\binom{n}{k} = \frac{n(n - 1) \cdots (n - k + 1)(n - k)(n - k - 1) \cdots 3 \cdot 2 \cdot 1}{k!(n - k)!}$$

$$= \frac{n!}{k!(n - k)!}.$$

This shows also that

$$\binom{n}{k} = \binom{n}{n-k}.$$

This is the so-called *symmetry property* of the binomial coefficients.
   The case $k = n$,

$$\binom{n}{n} = 1,$$

can be obtained from (3) as well as directly from the meaning of the binomial coefficient.
   Even though "n things, 0 at a time" is meaningless, it is customary to write

$$\binom{n}{0} = 1.$$

This convention is in accord with the symmetry property mentioned. Formula (4) agrees with this convention if we write $0! = 1$ by way of definition.
   Let us finally compare the two solutions of our problem. The binomial coefficients just introduced give the following interesting connection:

$$\binom{n}{0} + \binom{n}{1} + \cdots + \binom{n}{n-1} + \binom{n}{n} = 2^n.$$

(Cf. 1902/1, Note 2.)

   d) A useful property of two consecutive binomial coefficients, namely

$$\binom{n}{k} + \binom{n}{k+1} = \binom{n+1}{k+1},$$

is easily derived by writing the left side with a common denominator:

$$\frac{n(n-1)\cdots(n-k+1)}{k!} + \frac{n(n-1)\cdots(n-k+1)(n-k)}{(k+1)!}$$

$$= \frac{n(n-1)\cdots(n-k+1)(k+1) + n(n-1)\cdots(n-k+1)(n-k)}{(k+1)!}$$

$$= \frac{n(n-1)\cdots(n-k+1)[(k+1)+(n-k)]}{(k+1)!}$$

$$= \frac{n(n-1)\cdots(n-k+1)(n+1)}{(k+1)!} = \binom{n+1}{k+1}.$$

This relation can be derived directly from the definition.

1895/2. Given a right triangle ABC, construct a point N inside the triangle such that the angles NBC, NCA and NAB are equal.

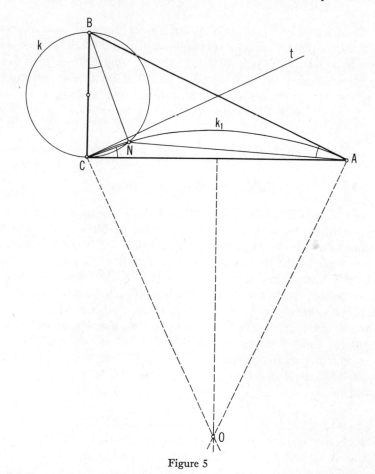

Figure 5

First Solution. a) *Analysis of the problem.* Denote the angles of the triangle ABC by α, β, γ, with $\gamma = 90°$ (Figure 5), and denote by N a point for which

$$\angle NBC = \angle NCA = \angle NAB.$$

Then

$$\angle BNC = 180° - (\angle BCN + \angle NBC)$$

$$= 180° - (\angle BCN + \angle NCA)$$

$$= 180° - \gamma;$$

and similarly,

$$\sphericalangle ANC = 180° - \alpha, \qquad \sphericalangle ANB = 180° - \beta.$$

b) *Construction of the point N.* With BC as diameter, construct a circle k. At the point A, draw a ray perpendicular to AB and lying on the same side of AB as the point C. It makes the angle $90°-\alpha$ with CA. At C, draw another ray making an angle $90°-\alpha$ with CA and intersecting the first ray in the point O. With O as center and OC as radius, draw the minor arc k_1 of the chord CA. The intersection of k_1 and k is the point N.

c) *Proof that N is the desired point.* Since in our case,

$$\sphericalangle BNC = 180° - \gamma = 90°,$$

the point N must lie on the circle k. The arc k_1 is the locus of all points P such that $\sphericalangle APC = 180°-\alpha$ and on the same side of line CA as B; see Note below. We must prove that the circle k and the arc k_1 have a common point inside the triangle. We note first that the point C cannot be the only common point of the two circles; for, if it were, they would have a common tangent at C. But the line AC is a tangent to k and a chord of the other circle. Therefore, there exists another point N common to the two circles. Since the circle k lies on the same side of AC as the point B, the point N is also on that side of AC. N must therefore lie on the arc k_1 of the other circle. If we show that the entire arc k_1 lies inside triangle ABC, we shall have proved that N lies inside triangle ABC. To this end, observe that AB is tangent to k_1 at A because AB is perpendicular to the radius AO at A. AB makes the angle α with AC. Similarly, the tangent t of the arc k_1 at C makes an angle α with CA. Since $\alpha < 90°$, this shows that the entire arc k_1 is inside triangle ABC.

Angles NBC and NCA intercept the same arc CN of circle k. Angles NCA and NAB intercept the same arc NA of the other circle. Therefore,

$$\sphericalangle NBC = \sphericalangle NCA = \sphericalangle NAB.$$

Note. The locus of points P at which a given line segment XY subtends a given angle. i) Let β be the given angle, $0° < \beta < 180°$, and let P be a point for which $\sphericalangle XPY = \beta$. Consider the circle about the triangle XPY. All but the end points of the arc XPY (which we shall call k') of this circle belong to the desired locus. (The end points do not form a triangle with X and Y.) For, if Q is a point on the arc XPY, the peripheral angles $\sphericalangle XPY$ and $\sphericalangle XQY$ are equal. Clearly, the same holds for points on the reflection k of k' in the segment XY; see Figure 6.

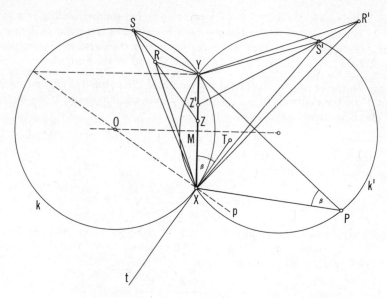

Figure 6

We shall now show that only k and k' belong to the locus sought. Clearly, points of the segment XY do not belong. For reasons of symmetry, it will now suffice to investigate those points of the plane lying on one side of the line through X and Y. Take the side containing k, and consider first a point inside the circle containing k, such as the point R in the figure. Let Z be an inner point of the segment XY; then the line through Z and R meets k in some point S. $\angle XRZ$ and $\angle ZRY$ are exterior angles respectively of $\triangle XRS$ and $\triangle YRS$; hence they are bigger than the interior angles at S. Since together they form the angle XRY,

$$\angle XRY = \angle XRZ + \angle ZRY > \angle XSZ + \angle ZSY = \angle XSY = \beta.$$

Thus R is not in the locus. Similarly, if a point is outside the circle, such as R' in the figure, then the segment $R'Z'$ contains an inner point S' which belongs to k', so that

$$\angle XR'Y = \angle XR'Z' + \angle Z'R'Y < \angle XS'Z' + \angle Z'S'Y = \angle XS'Y = \beta.$$

Thus R' is not in the locus.

We have thus shown that *the locus in question consists of two arcs between X and Y, symmetrical about the segment XY. The points X, Y do not belong to it. If β is a right angle, the locus is a circle of diameter XY.*

ii) The locus is easy to construct. For example, we can use the symmetry about XY and about the perpendicular bisector of XY, and the fact that the tangent to k at X forms the angle β with $X.Y$. Thus, we can draw the line

t at X for which $\measuredangle YXT = \beta$ (T a point on t) and the perpendicular p to t at X. Let the perpendicular bisector of XY meet p in the point O. Draw a circle of radius OX about O. Let k be that arc of the circle not intercepted by $\measuredangle TXY = \beta$. Reflecting k in XY gives k' and so the entire locus.

iii) In the sequel we shall need the length of the radius OX of this circle. Let M be the midpoint of XY; we can compute the length of OX by means of the right triangle MOX as follows:

$$\frac{XM}{OX} = \frac{XY}{2OX} = \sin \measuredangle MOX;$$

hence

$$OX = \frac{XY}{2 \sin \measuredangle MOX}.$$

The central angle subtending k is 2β if $\beta > 90°$ and $360° - 2\beta$ if $\beta < 90°$. Therefore $\measuredangle MOX = \frac{1}{2}\measuredangle XOY$ is either β or $180° - \beta$. Since $\sin(180° - \beta) = \sin \beta$, in either case

$$\sin \measuredangle MOX = \sin \frac{\measuredangle XOY}{2} = \sin \beta.$$

It follows that

$$OX = \frac{XY}{2 \sin \beta}.$$

Second Solution. Again we observe that the point N must lie on the circle k with BC as diameter. To find the exact position of N, we shall determine the direction of the line AN by using the condition

(1) $$\measuredangle NBC = \measuredangle NAB;$$

see Figure 7.

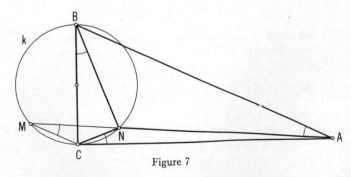

Figure 7

Any ray drawn from A into the interior of triangle ABC intersects the circle k in two points, N and M. Angles NBC and AMC are equal because each intercepts the arc CN. Hence, by (1),

$$\angle AMC = \angle NAB = \angle MAB.$$

But this implies that AB is parallel to MC.

Thus, N may be constructed as follows:

Draw a line through C parallel to AB. This line must intersect the circle k at some point other than C, say M. Draw MA; the desired point N is the intersection of the line MA with the circle k. By construction, M lies outside triangle ABC and N inside, as required by the problem.

Note. Brocard points. Given an arbitrary triangle ABC; it is possible, in a similar manner, to find two points N_1 and N_2 inside triangle ABC such that

$$\angle N_1BC = \angle N_1CA = \angle N_1AB,$$

and

$$\angle N_2CB = \angle N_2AC = \angle N_2BA.$$

N_1 and N_2 are called the *Brocard points* of the triangle.†

1895/3. Given the following information about a triangle: the radius R of its circumscribed circle, the length c of one of its sides, and the ratio a/b of the lengths of the other two sides; determine all three sides and angles of this triangle.

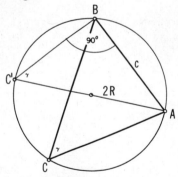

Figure 8

First Solution. The angle γ opposite the side c is found from the formula

$$\sin \gamma = \frac{c}{2R} ;$$

see Figure 8. If $c < 2R$, there are two possible values for γ, and if $c = 2R$,

---

† After the French mathematician and meteorologist Brocard (1845–1922).

there is only one; c cannot be greater than $2R$ since the triangle is in-scribed in the circle. For each value of γ so found, the other parts of the triangle can be determined as follows:

By the law of tangents (cf. the Note below)

$$\frac{\tan \frac{1}{2}(\alpha + \beta)}{\tan \frac{1}{2}(\alpha - \beta)} = \frac{a + b}{a - b} = \frac{(a/b) + 1}{(a/b) - 1},$$

where α and β are the angles opposite the sides a and b, respectively. Since

$$\frac{\alpha + \beta}{2} = \frac{180° - \gamma}{2},$$

we can express $(\alpha - \beta)/2$ in terms of a/b. Thus $(\alpha + \beta)/2$ and $(\alpha - \beta)/2$ are known; hence α and β may be obtained from

(1) $$\alpha = \frac{\alpha + \beta}{2} + \frac{\alpha - \beta}{2}, \qquad \beta = \frac{\alpha + \beta}{2} - \frac{\alpha - \beta}{2}.$$

Finally, the law of sines yields

$$a = \frac{c \sin \alpha}{\sin \gamma}, \qquad b = \frac{c \sin \beta}{\sin \gamma}.$$

Note. The law of tangents. We shall now prove the theorem used in the above solution. The law of sines can be written in the form

$$\frac{a}{\sin \alpha} = \frac{b}{\sin \beta}.$$

Let us denote the common value of these fractions by λ (λ is equal to the diameter of the circumscribed circle, i.e. $\lambda = 2R$) so that

then $$a = \lambda \sin \alpha, \qquad b = \lambda \sin \beta;$$

$$\frac{a + b}{a - b} = \frac{\lambda(\sin \alpha + \sin \beta)}{\lambda(\sin \alpha - \sin \beta)} = \frac{\sin \alpha + \sin \beta}{\sin \alpha - \sin \beta}.$$

Let us write α and β as sums of two angles, see equation (1), and let us ex-press $\sin \alpha$ and $\sin \beta$ by the formula for the sine of the sum of two angles. Then we obtain

$$\frac{\sin \alpha + \sin \beta}{\sin \alpha - \sin \beta} = \frac{2 \sin \frac{1}{2}(\alpha + \beta) \cos \frac{1}{2}(\alpha - \beta)}{2 \cos \frac{1}{2}(\alpha + \beta) \sin \frac{1}{2}(\alpha - \beta)} = \frac{\sin \frac{1}{2}(\alpha + \beta)}{\cos \frac{1}{2}(\alpha + \beta)} \cdot \frac{\cos \frac{1}{2}(\alpha - \beta)}{\sin \frac{1}{2}(\alpha - \beta)}$$

$$= \frac{\tan \frac{1}{2}(\alpha + \beta)}{\tan \frac{1}{2}(\alpha - \beta)}.$$

Thus

$$\frac{a+b}{a-b} = \frac{\tan\frac{1}{2}(\alpha+\beta)}{\tan\frac{1}{2}(\alpha-\beta)}.$$

Second Solution. Let O be the center of the circumscribed circle of triangle ABC; see Figure 9. Let C_1 be the foot of the perpendicular from O to AB; C_1 bisects AB. The theorems on inscribed and central angles and intercepted arcs, when applied to the arc AB, show that $\measuredangle BOC_1 = \measuredangle ACB = \gamma$. Hence

$$\sin\gamma = \frac{BC_1}{OB} = \frac{c/2}{R} = \frac{c}{2R}.$$

If $c < 2R$, this equation has two solutions; one yields an acute angle, the other an obtuse angle. If $c = 2R$, then $\gamma = 90°$. For each value of γ so determined, the rest of the triangle can be found as follows:

Drop a perpendicular from another vertex, say from B, to the opposite side AC and denote its foot by M_2. Then

$$BM_2 = a\sin\gamma \quad \left(=a\frac{c}{2R}\right)$$

and

$$CM_2 = a\cos\gamma \quad \left(=a\frac{\pm\sqrt{4R^2 - c^2}}{2R}\right).$$

The positive root in the parentheses corresponds to an acute angle γ, the negative root to an obtuse γ. Also

$$AM_2 = b - CM_2 = b - a\cos\gamma.$$

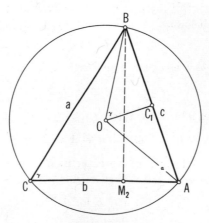

Figure 9

We have

$$\tan \alpha = \frac{BM_2}{AM_2} = \frac{a \sin \gamma}{b - a \cos \gamma} = \frac{(a/b) \sin \gamma}{1 - (a/b) \cos \gamma}.$$

This formula holds also if α is an obtuse angle. In this case AM_2 is considered negative and $b - a \cos \gamma$ is negative.

The angle β is obtained from

$$\alpha + \beta + \gamma = 180°.$$

Finally, from the law of sines,

$$a = \frac{c \sin \alpha}{\sin \gamma} = 2R \sin \alpha, \qquad b = \frac{c \sin \beta}{\sin \gamma} = 2R \sin \beta.$$

1896 Competition

1896/1. Prove that

$$\log n \geq k \cdot \log 2,$$

where n is a natural number and k the number of distinct primes that divide n.

Solution. Let n be a natural number greater than 1, let $p_1, p_2, \cdots, p_k$ be its prime† divisors, and let

$$p_1^{\alpha_1}, \quad p_2^{\alpha_2}, \quad \cdots, \quad p_k^{\alpha_k}$$

be the highest powers of these primes that divide n.

Then (see Note below)

$$n = p_1^{\alpha_1} p_2^{\alpha_2} \cdots p_k^{\alpha_k}.$$

Since none of the p_i is less than 2 and each $\alpha_i \geq 1$,

$$n \geq 2^{\alpha_1 + \alpha_2 + \cdots + \alpha_k} \geq 2^k.$$

This is true also for $n = 1$, for then

$$k = 0 \quad \text{and} \quad n = 1 = 2^0 = 2^k.$$

If the base a of the logarithm is greater than 1, for instance if $a = 10$, then our inequality gives the desired result:

$$\log_a n \geq k \cdot \log_a 2.$$

† By "prime", we shall always mean *positive* prime.

Note. Factorization into a product of powers of primes. (For definitions of "prime" and "composite number", see Note to the First Solution of
1894/1.)

Every composite natural number is the product of two or more primes.

The smallest composite number is $4 = 2 \cdot 2$; in order to prove the above
theorem it suffices to show that, if the theorem holds for all composite natural
numbers less than some composite natural number a, then it holds also for a.
(Complete induction.)

Indeed, according to the definition of composite number (see 1894/1,
page 19), a is a product of two factors, k and b, from among the numbers

$$2, \quad 3, \quad \cdots, \quad a - 1.$$

If the theorem holds for all composite natural numbers less than a, then k
and b are either primes or products of primes. Therefore, $a = kb$ can also be
written as a product of primes.

Every natural number is the product of non-negative powers of primes.

For a given composite natural number a, one finds the prime power factors
by first finding the prime factors, grouping equal ones together, and writing
the factors in each group as a power. For example

$$120 = 2 \cdot 2 \cdot 2 \cdot 3 \cdot 5$$
$$= 2^3 \cdot 3^1 \cdot 5^1.$$

Since the zeroth power of any number is 1, we may, of course, add primes to
the zeroth power in such a factorization, e.g.,

$$120 = 2^3 \cdot 3^1 \cdot 5^1 \cdot 7^0 \cdot 11^0.$$

A prime p can be written as a product of the first power of p (that is, p^1),
and the zeroth power of any other primes.

Finally, 1 can be written as a product of any number of primes to the
zeroth power.

With these agreements, the factorization of natural numbers into powers
of primes is *unique*. In other words:

If

(1) $$a = p_1^{\alpha_1} p_2^{\alpha_2} \cdots p_k^{\alpha_k},$$

*where the p_i are distinct primes and the α_i non-negative integers, then α_i is the
highest power of p_i which divides a; hence, the factorization (1) of a is its only
factorization (except for the order of the factors and the appearance of an arbitrary
number of primes to the power zero).*

The proof of this useful and by no means trivial theorem (known as the
Fundamental Theorem of Arithmetic) follows from the theorem: *If none of
the factors of a product is divisible by a prime number p, then the product itself
is not divisible by p* [see 1894/1, Solution 2, Note, b)].

We shall prove that a number a cannot have two distinct prime power
factorizations, that is two factorizations in which a prime, say p, occurs with
two different multiplicities. (The multiplicity zero is also admitted here.)

Suppose, to the contrary, that

(2)
$$a = p^\alpha \cdot v = p^\beta \cdot w$$

with $\alpha > \beta \geq 0$, and where the prime factorizations of v and w contain no positive power of p. Then, by the theorem quoted above, v and w are not divisible by p. But it follows from (2) that

$$w = v \cdot p^{\alpha-\beta}, \qquad \text{with} \quad \alpha - \beta > 0,$$

i.e., that w is divisible by p. We are led to a contradiction and so our assumption is false; thus all factorizations of a must contain the prime p to the same power.

1896/2. Prove that the equations

$$x^2 - 3xy + 2y^2 + x - y = 0$$

and

$$x^2 - 2xy + y^2 - 5x + 7y = 0$$

imply the equation

$$xy - 12x + 15y = 0.$$

First Solution. The first of these equations can be written in the form

$$(x - y)(x - 2y + 1) = 0.$$

Hence the given system of equations is satisfied by those pairs of values (x, y) which satisfy either

$$x - y = 0$$

(1)

$$x^2 - 2xy + y^2 - 5x + 7y = 0$$

or

$$x - 2y + 1 = 0$$

(2)

$$x^2 - 2xy + y^2 - 5x + 7y = 0.$$

From the first equation of system (1), we obtain

$$x = y;$$

substituting this result in the second equation, we obtain

$$2y = 0.$$

Hence the only solution of (1) is $x = 0$ and $y = 0$.

From the first equation of system (2), we find

$$x = 2y - 1;$$

substituting this result in the second equation, we obtain

$$(2y - 1)^2 - 2(2y - 1)y + y^2 - 5(2y - 1) + 7y = 0.$$

After some manipulations, this takes the form:

$$y^2 - 5y + 6 = 0,$$

and is satisfied by $y = 2$ or by $y = 3$. The corresponding values of $x = 2y - 1$ are 3 and 5. Hence the solutions are

$$x = 3, \quad y = 2, \quad \text{and} \quad x = 5, \quad y = 3.$$

Therefore, the originally given system of equations has three solutions:

$$x = 0, \quad y = 0; \quad x = 3, \quad y = 2; \quad x = 5, \quad y = 3.$$

A straightforward computation shows that these values satisfy the equation

$$xy - 12x + 15y = 0.$$

Second Solution. We consider the identity

$$(x^2 - 3xy + 2y^2 + x - y)(x - y - 9)$$
$$+ (x^2 - 2xy + y^2 - 5x + 7y)(-x + 2y + 3)$$
$$= 2(xy - 12x + 15y).$$

This shows immediately that, if the first and second equations of our problem are satisfied, the left hand side of the third equation is zero.

1896/3. Construct a triangle, given the feet of its altitudes. Express the lengths of the sides of the solution triangle Y in terms of the lengths of the sides of the triangle X whose vertices are the feet of the altitudes of triangle Y.

Solution in the case that Y is an acute triangle. *Definition.* A triangle X whose vertices are the feet of the altitudes of another triangle Y is called the *orthic triangle* of Y.†

---

† More generally, if from a point P inside a triangle Y three perpendiculars are dropped to the sides of Y, then the triangle whose vertices are the feet of these perpendiculars is called a *pedal triangle* of Y. If the point P happens to be the *orthocenter* (i.e., the intersection of the altitudes of Y), the resulting pedal triangle is the orthic triangle.

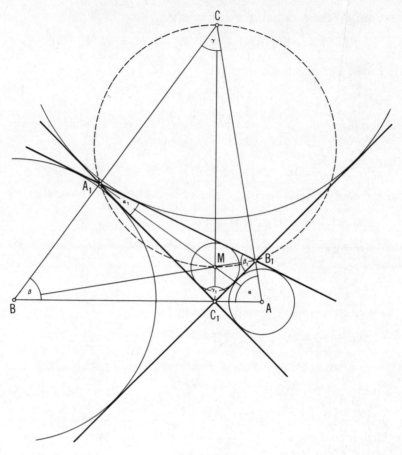

Figure 10

a) THEOREM. *The altitudes of an acute triangle ABC bisect the vertex angles of its orthic triangle.*

If the altitudes AA_1 and BB_1 intersect in M, then A_1MC and CMB_1 are right triangles with hypotenuse CM (see Figure 10). Therefore A_1 and B_1 lie on a circle k_C with CM as diameter. Moreover, if α, β, γ denote the vertex angles of $\triangle ABC$, then

$$\angle MCB_1 = 90° - \alpha,$$

$$\angle CMB_1 = \alpha = \angle BMC_1,$$

$$\angle MBC_1 = 90° - \alpha.$$

The arc MB_1 of the circle k_C is intercepted by the inscribed angles MA_1B_1

and MCB_1. Thus

$$\sphericalangle MA_1B_1 = \sphericalangle MCB_1 = 90° - \alpha,$$

that is,

$$\sphericalangle AA_1B_1 = 90° - \alpha.$$

Similarly, by considering the circle k_B with diameter BM, we see that

$$\sphericalangle MA_1C_1 = \sphericalangle MBC_1 = 90° - \alpha,$$

that is

$$\sphericalangle AA_1C_1 = 90° - \alpha,$$

so that AA_1 indeed bisects the vertex angle at A_1 of the orthic triangle; the same reasoning yields the desired results for the other angles of the orthic triangle. Incidentally, denoting the angles of the orthic triangle $A_1B_1C_1$ by $\alpha_1, \beta_1, \gamma_1$, we have the result

$$\frac{\alpha_1}{2} = 90° - \alpha, \qquad \frac{\beta_1}{2} = 90° - \beta, \qquad \frac{\gamma_1}{2} = 90° - \gamma.$$

The theorem just proved, together with the fact that the angle bisectors of a triangle meet in a point, also shows that the three altitudes of $\triangle ABC$ meet in a point; this point is called the *orthocenter* of $\triangle ABC$, and is the center of the circle inscribed in $\triangle A_1B_1C_1$.

b) *Construction.* According to a) there is just one solution to our problem, namely that triangle ABC whose vertices are obtained by bisecting the exterior angles of triangle $A_1B_1C_1$ and determining the intersections of these bisectors. In other words the points A, B, C are just the centers of the circles which are tangent to one side of $A_1B_1C_1$ from the outside, and to the other two from the inside.†

c) *Justification of the Construction.* Let us construct also the bisectors of the interior angles of $\triangle A_1B_1C_1$. The bisectors of two exterior angles at two vertices and that of the interior angle at the third vertex meet at one point. This can be seen, for example, by observing that the point A (see Figure 10) is equidistant from the lines A_1B_1 and B_1C_1 and also from A_1C_1 and B_1C_1, so the locus of points equidistant from A_1C_1 and A_1B_1 must also go through A. On the other hand, the bisector of our exterior angle and that of an adjacent interior angle (the supplement)

---

† These circles (see Figure 10) are called *exterior circles* or *excircles*, and their centers are called *excenters* of triangle $A_1B_1C_1$.

are perpendicular. Thus AA_1, BB_1, and CC_1 are perpendicular, respectively, to BC, CA, and AB. Thus A_1, B_1, C_1 are indeed the feet of the altitudes of $\triangle ABC$.

d) *Computation.* We saw in a) that

$$\frac{\alpha_1}{2} = 90° - \alpha;$$

thus [cf. formula (12) in Note 2 below],

$$\cos \alpha = \sin (90° - \alpha) = \sin \frac{\alpha_1}{2} = \sqrt{\frac{(s_1 - b_1)(s_1 - c_1)}{b_1 c_1}}$$

where s_1 is half the perimeter of $\triangle A_1 B_1 C_1$, i.e., $s_1 = \frac{1}{2}(a_1 + b_1 + c_1)$.

Moreover, $\triangle C_1 A B_1$ is similar to $\triangle CAB$ because both have the angle α in common and

$$\angle C_1 B_1 A = 90° - \frac{\beta_1}{2} = \beta = \angle CBA.$$

Hence

$$\frac{B_1 C_1}{BC} = \frac{C_1 A}{CA} = \cos \alpha$$

that is

$$\frac{a_1}{a} = \cos \alpha.$$

With the aid of formula (12) of Note 2 below, this gives

$$a = \frac{a_1}{\cos \alpha} = a_1 \sqrt{\frac{b_1 c_1}{(s_1 - b_1)(s_1 - c_1)}}.$$

Similarly

$$b = \frac{b_1}{\cos \beta} = b_1 \sqrt{\frac{a_1 c_1}{(s_1 - a_1)(s_1 - c_1)}},$$

$$c = \frac{c_1}{\cos \gamma} = c_1 \sqrt{\frac{a_1 b_1}{(s_1 - a_1)(s_1 - b_1)}}.$$

Note 1. On the orthic triangle of an obtuse triangle.   In an obtuse triangle (just as in an acute triangle), the altitude from the obtuse vertex bisects the interior angle of that vertex of the orthic triangle which is the foot of that altitude. However, the altitudes drawn from the other two vertices bisect the corresponding exterior angles of the orthic triangle.

If we admit also obtuse triangles as solutions, then we obtain, in addition to $\triangle ABC$, the triangles BCM, CAM, ABM satisfying our conditions. The altitudes belonging to these triangles meet, respectively, at the points A, B, C. In other words, the orthocenters of triangles BCM, CAM, ABM (and ABC) are A, B, C (and M) respectively.

All four solutions have this in common: The vertices and the orthocenter of each solution triangle are centers of just those circles which are tangent to every side of $\triangle A_1B_1C_1$.

For the acute solution, $\triangle ABC$, the *orthocenter* is the center of the circle that touches every side of $\triangle A_1B_1C_1$ from the *inside*.

For the obtuse solutions, triangles BCM, CAM, ABM, the *obtuse vertex* is the center of the circle that touches every side of $\triangle A_1B_1C_1$ from the *inside*.

Note 2. a) On circles tangent to the sides of a triangle. Let O be the center and r the radius of the circle k tangent to the sides of $\triangle ABC$ from the inside, and let D, E, F be the points of tangency on BC, CA, AB, respectively; see Figure 11. Let k_a be the circle tangent to the extensions of sides AB and AC and to side BC and let the corresponding data for k_a be O_a, r_a and D', E', F'. Moreover, denote the lengths of the sides AB, BC and CA by c, a and b, and let the perimeter be $2s = a + b + c$.

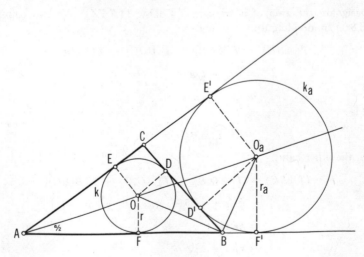

Figure 11

Since a pair of tangents from a point to a circle have equal lengths, we have

$$AE = AF, \quad BF = BD, \quad CD = CE.$$

Hence

$$2s = AB + BC + CA = 2(AE + BF + CD),$$

or

$$s = AE + BF + CD$$

so that

(1) $\qquad CD = s - (AE + BF) = s - (AF + BF) = s - c.$

Similarly,

$$AE = s - a, \quad BF = s - b.$$

For the circle k_a,

$$
\begin{aligned}
2AE' = AE' + AF' &= AC + CE' + AB + BF' \\
&= AB + AC + CD' + BD' \\
&= AB + AC + BC \\
&= 2s
\end{aligned}
$$

so that

(2) $\qquad\qquad\qquad AE' = AF' = s$

and

(3) $\qquad CE' = AE' - AC = s - b, \quad BF' = s - c.$

Designate the area of a triangle XYZ by $T(XYZ)$. We can compute $T(ABC)$ by dividing up the triangle:

$$
\begin{aligned}
T(ABC) &= T(AOB) + T(BOC) + T(COA) \\
&= \tfrac{1}{2}rc + \tfrac{1}{2}ra + \tfrac{1}{2}rb \\
&= \tfrac{1}{2}r(a + b + c),
\end{aligned}
$$

that is

(4) $\qquad\qquad\qquad T(ABC) = rs.$

On the other hand,

(5) $\qquad T(ABC) = T(AO_aB) + T(AO_aC) - T(BO_aC)$

$$
\begin{aligned}
&= \tfrac{1}{2}r_ac + \tfrac{1}{2}r_ab - \tfrac{1}{2}r_aa \\
&= \tfrac{1}{2}r_a(b + c - a) \\
&= r_a(s - a).
\end{aligned}
$$

Similarly,

(6) $\qquad\qquad\qquad T(ABC) = r_b(s - b),$

and

(7) $$T(ABC) = r_c(s - c),$$

where r_b, r_c stand for the radii of the circles k_b, k_c tangent to sides b, respectively c, and the extensions of the other two sides of $\triangle ABC$.

b) **Connection between the angles and the sides of a triangle.**
We know that the center of the inscribed circle of a triangle is the point of intersection of the angle bisectors, so that, for example $\sphericalangle OAF = \frac{1}{2}\alpha$. Using (4) and Heron's formula† for the area of a triangle, we obtain

$$\tan\frac{\alpha}{2} = \frac{OF}{AF} = \frac{r}{s - a} = \frac{T(ABC)}{s(s - a)}$$

(8)
$$= \frac{\sqrt{s(s - a)(s - b)(s - c)}}{s(s - a)}$$

$$= \sqrt{\frac{(s - b)(s - c)}{s(s - a)}}.$$

Similarly,

(9) $$\tan\frac{\beta}{2} = \sqrt{\frac{(s - a)(s - c)}{s(s - b)}}$$

and

(10) $$\tan\frac{\gamma}{2} = \sqrt{\frac{(s - a)(s - b)}{s(s - c)}}.$$

But, using the fact that the area of a triangle is half the product of its base and altitude and considering c as the base and expressing the altitude from C as $b \sin \alpha$, we also have

$$T(ABC) = \frac{1}{2} bc \sin \alpha = bc \sin\frac{\alpha}{2}\cos\frac{\alpha}{2} = bc \tan\frac{\alpha}{2}\cos^2\frac{\alpha}{2}$$

which, together with (8) and Heron's formula gives

$$bc \cos^2\frac{\alpha}{2} = \frac{T(ABC)}{\tan\frac{1}{2}(\alpha)} = s(s - a).$$

In this way we get, one after the other,

(11) $$\cos\frac{\alpha}{2} = \sqrt{\frac{s(s - a)}{bc}}, \quad \cos\frac{\beta}{2} = \sqrt{\frac{s(s - b)}{ac}}, \quad \cos\frac{\gamma}{2} = \sqrt{\frac{s(s - c)}{ab}}.$$

† See footnote on page 23.

Since $\sin(\alpha/2) = \tan(\alpha/2)\cos(\alpha/2)$, (11) and (8), (9), (10) yield

(12)
$$\sin\frac{\alpha}{2} = \sqrt{\frac{(s-b)(s-c)}{bc}}, \qquad \sin\frac{\beta}{2} = \sqrt{\frac{(s-a)(s-c)}{ac}},$$

$$\sin\frac{\gamma}{2} = \sqrt{\frac{(s-a)(s-b)}{ab}}.$$

1897 Competition

1897/1. Prove, for the angles α, β and γ of a right triangle, the following relation:

$$\sin\alpha\sin\beta\sin(\alpha-\beta) + \sin\beta\sin\gamma\sin(\beta-\gamma) + \sin\gamma\sin\alpha\sin(\gamma-\alpha)$$
$$+ \sin(\alpha-\beta)\sin(\beta-\gamma)\sin(\gamma-\alpha) = 0.$$

Solution. Let $\alpha = 90° = \beta + \gamma$. Then

$$\sin\alpha = 1, \quad \sin(\alpha-\beta) = \sin\gamma, \quad \sin(\gamma-\alpha) = -\sin(\alpha-\gamma) = -\sin\beta$$

Therefore

$$\sin\alpha\sin\beta\sin(\alpha-\beta) = \sin\beta\sin\gamma,$$

$$\sin\beta\sin\gamma\sin(\beta-\gamma) = \sin\beta\sin\gamma\sin(\beta-\gamma),$$

$$\sin\gamma\sin\alpha\sin(\gamma-\alpha) = -\sin\gamma\sin\beta,$$

$$\sin(\alpha-\beta)\sin(\beta-\gamma)\sin(\gamma-\alpha) = -\sin\gamma\sin(\beta-\gamma)\sin\beta,$$

and the sum of these four products is zero.

Note. Relation between sums and products of trigonometric functions. We claim that the formula of the above problem is valid for arbitrary angles α, β and γ; that is, we claim that

$$\sin\alpha\sin\beta\sin(\alpha-\beta) + \sin\beta\sin\gamma\sin(\beta-\gamma) + \sin\gamma\sin\alpha\sin(\gamma-\alpha)$$

(1)
$$+ \sin(\alpha-\beta)\sin(\beta-\gamma)\sin(\gamma-\alpha) = 0$$

holds, not only for the angles of an arbitrary triangle, but for *any* three angles α, β, γ. We shall prove this by transforming the products of the trigonometric functions occurring in (1) into sums of trigonometric functions.

a) The formulas for the sine and cosine of the sum of two angles lead to the following relations between trigonometric sums and products:

$$\sin (x + y) + \sin (x - y) = 2 \sin x \cos y$$
$$\cos (x - y) + \cos (x + y) = 2 \cos x \cos y$$
$$\cos (x - y) - \cos (x + y) = 2 \sin x \sin y.$$

Hence

$$\sin x \sin y = \tfrac{1}{2}[\cos (x - y) - \cos (x + y)],$$
$$\cos x \cos y = \tfrac{1}{2}[\cos (x - y) + \cos (x + y)],$$
$$\sin x \cos y = \tfrac{1}{2}[\sin (x + y) + \sin (x - y)];$$

in particular for $x = y$, these reduce to

$$\sin^2 x = \tfrac{1}{2}[1 - \cos 2x], \quad \cos^2 x = \tfrac{1}{2}[1 + \cos 2x], \quad \sin x \cos x = \tfrac{1}{2} \sin 2x.$$

By repeated application of these formulas, products of an arbitrary number of sines and cosines may be transformed into sums.

Each term of (1) is the product of three sines. The product of three sines can be transformed into a sum as follows:

$$\sin x \sin y \sin z = \tfrac{1}{2}[\cos (x - y) - \cos (x + y)] \sin z$$
$$= \tfrac{1}{2}[\cos (x - y) \sin z - \cos (x + y) \sin z]$$
$$= \tfrac{1}{4}[\sin (x - y + z) + \sin (-x + y + z)$$
(2)
$$- \sin (x + y + z) - \sin (-x - y + z)]$$
$$= \tfrac{1}{4}[\sin (-x + y + z) + \sin (x - y + z)$$
$$+ \sin (x + y - z) - \sin (x + y + z)].$$

b) Now, if $x = \alpha - \beta$, $y = \beta - \gamma$, $z = \gamma - \alpha$, then

$$x + y + z = 0, \qquad -x + y + z = -2(\alpha - \beta),$$
$$x - y + z = -2(\beta - \gamma), \qquad x + y - z = -2(\gamma - \alpha).$$

Hence (2) yields

$$4 \sin (\alpha - \beta) \sin (\beta - \gamma) \sin (\gamma - \alpha)$$
(3)
$$= - \sin 2(\alpha - \beta) - \sin 2(\beta - \gamma) - \sin 2(\gamma - \alpha).$$

Since this relation holds for arbitrary angles α, β and γ, we may insert 0 successively for γ, α, and β in (3) and obtain

$$(4) \qquad 4 \sin \alpha \sin \beta \sin (\alpha - \beta) = \sin 2(\alpha - \beta) + \sin 2\beta - \sin 2\alpha$$

$$(5) \qquad 4 \sin \beta \sin \gamma \sin (\beta - \gamma) = \sin 2(\beta - \gamma) + \sin 2\gamma - \sin 2\beta$$

$$(6) \qquad 4 \sin \gamma \sin \alpha \sin (\gamma - \alpha) = \sin 2(\gamma - \alpha) + \sin 2\alpha - \sin 2\gamma.$$

If we add equations (3)–(6), we obtain formula (1).

1897/2. Show that, if α, β and γ are angles of an arbitrary triangle, then

$$\sin \frac{\alpha}{2} \sin \frac{\beta}{2} \sin \frac{\gamma}{2} < \frac{1}{4}.$$

First Solution. Since $\alpha + \beta + \gamma = 180°$, the angles $\alpha/2$, $\beta/2$, $\gamma/2$ are acute angles, and we know that when an acute angle increases, its sine increases. Hence the inequalities

$$\frac{\alpha}{2} = 90° - \frac{\beta + \gamma}{2} < 90° - \frac{\beta}{2} < 90°$$

imply the inequality

$$\sin \frac{\alpha}{2} \sin \frac{\beta}{2} < \sin \left(90° - \frac{\beta}{2}\right) \sin \frac{\beta}{2} = \cos \frac{\beta}{2} \sin \frac{\beta}{2} \, ;$$

and since

$$\cos \frac{\beta}{2} \sin \frac{\beta}{2} = \frac{1}{2} \sin \beta, \qquad \sin \beta \leq 1, \qquad \cos \beta \leq 1,$$

it follows that

$$(1) \qquad \sin \frac{\alpha}{2} \sin \frac{\beta}{2} < \frac{1}{2} \sin \beta \leq \frac{1}{2}.$$

Suppose γ is the smallest of the three angles; then $\gamma \leq 180°/3$ and $\gamma/2 \leq 30°$, so that

$$(2) \qquad \sin \frac{\gamma}{2} \leq \sin 30° = \frac{1}{2}.$$

From (1) and (2) we obtain

(3)
$$\sin\frac{\alpha}{2}\sin\frac{\beta}{2}\sin\frac{\gamma}{2} < \frac{1}{4}.$$

Second Solution.† a) It is known (cf. Note 1 below) that

$$\sin\frac{\alpha}{2}\sin\frac{\beta}{2}\sin\frac{\gamma}{2} = \frac{r}{4R},$$

where r is the radius of the incircle (inscribed circle) of the triangle with angles α, β, γ, and R is the radius of its circumcircle (circumscribed circle). Since clearly $r < R$, the product on the left side is less than $\frac{1}{4}$.

b) We shall sharpen the inequality (3) by showing that

(4)
$$\sin\frac{\alpha}{2}\sin\frac{\beta}{2}\sin\frac{\gamma}{2} \leq \frac{1}{8},$$

and we shall establish (4) by proving that $r \leq R/2$.

According to a theorem of Euler (cf. Note 2 below),

$$d^2 = R^2 - 2Rr,$$

where d is the distance between the center of the incircle and the center of the circumcircle. Hence

$$2Rr \leq R^2, \quad \text{and} \quad r \leq R/2.$$

If the triangle is equilateral, then $d = 0$ and the value of the product $\sin(\alpha/2)\sin(\beta/2)\sin(\gamma/2)$ is exactly $1/8$.

Note 1. The meaning of some trigonometric products. Let s denote the semiperimeter $\frac{1}{2}(a + b + c)$ of a triangle, t its area, R the radius of its circumcircle and r the radius of its incircle. Then the following formulas hold:

I
$$\tan\frac{\alpha}{2}\tan\frac{\beta}{2}\tan\frac{\gamma}{2} = \frac{t}{s^2}$$

or, since $t = sr$ [see e.g. eq. (4) in Note 2 of 1896/3],

II
$$\tan\frac{\alpha}{2}\tan\frac{\beta}{2}\tan\frac{\gamma}{2} = \frac{r}{s}.$$

† While this solution of the problem requires much more knowledge, it gives greater insight into the essence of the problem than the simple calculations of the first solution.

Also

III
$$\cos\frac{\alpha}{2}\cos\frac{\beta}{2}\cos\frac{\gamma}{2} = \frac{s}{4R},$$

and

IV
$$\sin\frac{\alpha}{2}\sin\frac{\beta}{2}\sin\frac{\gamma}{2} = \frac{r}{4R}.$$

In order to prove these, we make use of Note 2 to the solution of Problem 1896/3. From formulas (8), (9) and (10), see page 45, we obtain

$$\tan\frac{\alpha}{2}\tan\frac{\beta}{2}\tan\frac{\gamma}{2} = \frac{\sqrt{s(s-a)(s-b)(s-c)}}{s^2};$$

this, together with Heron's formula and eq. (4) on page 44 yields formulas I and II.

Equation (11) on page 45 yields

$$\cos\frac{\alpha}{2}\cos\frac{\beta}{2}\cos\frac{\gamma}{2} = \frac{s\sqrt{s(s-a)(s-b)(s-c)}}{abc} = \frac{st}{abc}$$

which, together with the relations

$$\sin\gamma = \frac{c}{2R}, \quad \text{that is,} \quad R = \frac{c}{2\sin\gamma} = \frac{abc}{4t}$$

(see Figure 8) implies formula III. Finally, formulas II and III imply formula IV.

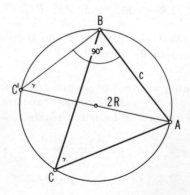

Figure 8

Note 2. The inscribed and circumscribed circles of a given triangle. Consider two circles, k and k', one containing the other, say k contains k'; see Figures 12 and 13. Let O and O' denote their centers, R and r their radii, and d the distance between O and O'.

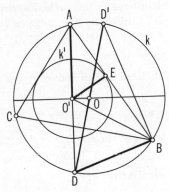

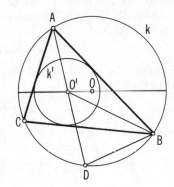

Figure 12   Figure 13

To the theorem of Euler† used in the Second Solution, part b) of this problem, we shall now add the converse and then prove the full theorem.

THEOREM. *A necessary and sufficient condition for the existence of a triangle with circumcircle k and incircle k′ is the equality*

$$(1) \qquad\qquad d^2 = R^2 - 2Rr.$$

PROOF: a) Let A be any point on the circle k (see Figure 12). What is a necessary and sufficient condition for the existence of points B and C such that the triangle ABC satisfies the requirements of the theorem? If there are such points B and C, they can be defined as the points of intersection of the circle k with the tangents drawn from A to $k′$. Triangle ABC will have $k′$ as its incircle if BC is also tangent to $k′$. A necessary and sufficient condition for BC to be tangent to $k′$ is

$$(2) \qquad\qquad \angle ABO′ = \angle O′BC.$$

(In the diagram of Figure 12, this condition is not satisfied.)

From (2) we shall now obtain some equivalent necessary and sufficient conditions.

---

† L. Euler was born in Basel, Switzerland, in 1707 and died in St. Petersburg (now Leningrad) in 1783. At the time of his death, he was director of the Mathematics Section of the Academy of Sciences there. His distinguished researches enriched almost all branches of mathematics. A significant portion of the mathematical notation in use today is due to him; for example, he introduced the use of the letter π for the ratio of circumference to diameter of a circle, and the letter e for the base of natural logarithms, i.e., e is the limit of the sequence

$$1 + 1, \quad \left(1 + \frac{1}{2}\right)^2, \quad \left(1 + \frac{1}{3}\right)^3, \quad \cdots, \quad \left(1 + \frac{1}{n}\right)^n, \quad \cdots.$$

Draw the line from A through O' until it intersects the circle k again, in the point D. Then AO' bisects the angle BAC made by the tangents from A to k'. That is

$$\angle O'AB = \angle CAO'.$$

Moreover $\angle CAO' = \angle CBD$ because both these angles intercept the arc CD of the circle k. Hence

(3) $$\angle O'AB = \angle CBD.$$

Since angles $O'AB$ and ABO' are interior angles of the triangle $O'AB$ opposite to the exterior angle $BO'D$, we have

$$\angle O'AB = \angle BO'D - \angle ABO'.$$

Furthermore, clearly

$$\angle CBD = \angle O'BD - \angle O'BC.$$

If we substitute these values for angles $O'AB$ and CBD into (3) we obtain

(4) $$\angle BO'D - \angle ABO' = \angle O'BD - \angle O'BC.$$

Thus condition (2) holds if and only if

(5) $$\angle BO'D = \angle O'BD.$$

These two angles are opposite the sides BD and $O'D$ of triangle $BO'D$, so that we can reformulate our result as follows:

Triangle ABC has the circle k' as incircle if and only if

$$BD = O'D.$$

(In the diagram of Figure 13, this condition is satisfied.)

b) In order to show the equivalence of this necessary and sufficient condition with the condition (1), we shall work with the ratio $BD/O'D$ and express it in terms of the quantities R, r and d.

Let E denote the point of tangency of the circle k' with the line AB (see Figure 12) and let D' denote the point diametrically opposite to D on the circle k. We claim that the triangles $AO'E$ and $D'DB$ are similar. This is a consequence of the following two facts:

i) they are right triangles, the right angles being at the vertices E and B, respectively;

ii) the angle at A of the first triangle is equal to the angle at D' of the second because both angles are inscribed in the circle k and intercept its arc BD.

From the similarity of triangles $AO'E$ and $D'DB$ it follows that

$$\frac{AO'}{EO'} = \frac{D'D}{BD}; \quad \text{that is,} \quad \frac{AO'}{r} = \frac{2R}{BD}$$

or

(6) $$AO' \cdot BD = 2Rr.$$

Next we apply the following corollary of the theorem on inscribed angles and their intercepted arcs: *If two chords of a circle intersect, then the product of the segments of one is equal to the product of the segments of the other.* Let AD be one of the chords of the circle k and let the diameter of k through the point O' be the other. Then, by this corollary,

(7) $$AO' \cdot O'D = (R+d) \cdot (R-d).$$

If we divide equation (6) by (7), we obtain

$$\frac{BD}{O'D} = \frac{2Rr}{(R+d)(R-d)}.$$

Clearly, BD is equal to $O'D$ if and only if

(8) $$2Rr = (R+d)(R-d).$$

c) The results of parts a) and b) can be summarized as follows:

If A is an arbitrary point on the circle k, then the necessary and sufficient condition for the existence of points B and C such that triangle ABC has k' as its incircle is that equation (8) *hold.*

This establishes Euler's theorem [since equation (8) is the same as equation (1)] and its converse.†

Finally, observe that condition (8) does not depend on the choice of the particular point A on the circle k. Therefore:

If for some point A of the circle k we can construct a triangle ABC having k as circumcircle and k' as incircle, then this construction is possible for any point A on k. This principle has been formulated by Poncelet‡ for arbitrary conic sections and for polygons instead of triangles as follows: Aut semper, aut nunquam (either always or never).

---

† See also the discussion of Euler's Theorem in *Geometric Inequalities* by N. D. Kazarinoff, in this series.

‡ The French general and mathematician J. V. Poncelet was born in Metz in 1788 and died in Paris in 1867. His main work was *Traité des propriétés projectives des figures* (1822). He was a member of the *Académie des Sciences* of the *Institut*.

The French *Institut* has five sections called "academies"; that concerned with mathematics and sciences is called *Académie des Sciences* and should not be confused with the *Académie Française* whose members are commonly referred to as "the 40 immortals". The *Académie Française* is the poetry and literature section of the *Institut*; however, distinguished thinkers in other fields are sometimes honored by election to the *Académie Française*. The famous mathematican H. Poincaré (1854–1912), for instance, was a member of both the *Académie des Sciences* and the *Académie Française*.

1897/3. Let $ABCD$ be a rectangle and let M, N and P, Q be the points of intersection of some line e with the sides AB, CD and AD, BC, respectively (or their extensions). Given the points M, N, P, Q and the length p of the side AB, construct the rectangle. Under what conditions can this problem be solved, and how many solutions does it have?

First Solution. Construct a right triangle PSQ with hypotenuse PQ and with $PS = p$; see Figure 14. Draw lines parallel to PS through the points M and N, draw lines perpendicular to PS through the points P and Q. Clearly, these four lines determine a rectangle which satisfies the requirements of the problem.

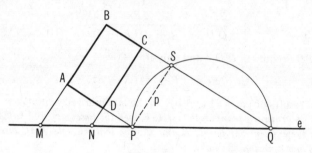

Figure 14

The problem has a solution only if the triangle PSQ can actually be constructed, that is if

$$p < PQ;$$

and if this condition is satisfied, triangle PSQ may be constructed on either side of the line e. Hence we get two solutions; each is a reflection of the other in the line e.

Second Solution. Before solving the problem, consider the following generalization: Let $ABCD$ be a parallelogram whose sides AB, CD, AD, BC (or their extensions) intersect a line e in the points M, N, P, Q, respectively; see Figure 15. Given the points M, N, P, Q, the length p of side AB, and the angles of the parallelogram, construct the parallelogram.

The first step is to construct the point of intersection S of the side BC with a line through P parallel to AB. Once this point S is found, the previous construction can be carried out easily.

We shall determine the point S from the following two conditions: Since $ABSP$ is a parallelogram, its opposite sides are equal; thus

$$PS = AB = p,$$

so that the point S lies on the circle with center at P and radius p.

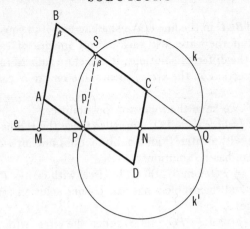

Figure 15

Moreover, AB is parallel to PS so that angle PSQ is equal either to the angle β at B, or to its supplement. We claim that, if the segments MN and PQ are oriented in the same sense (i.e. if either N is to the right of M and Q to the right of P, or if N is to the left of M and Q to the left of P), then

$$\sphericalangle PSQ = \beta,$$

and if MN and PQ are oppositely oriented, then

$$\sphericalangle PSQ = 180° - \beta;$$

see Figures 15 and 16. In either case, the locus of points S for which $\sphericalangle PSQ = \beta$ (or $180° - \beta$) consists of arcs k and k', one above PQ, the other below PQ. (The arcs can be constructed by the method explained in the Note to the First Solution of Problem 1895/2, and the radius of the circle of which k (or k') is an arc has length $PQ/(2 \sin \beta)$; see iii of that same Note, page 32.) Thus, the desired point S is a point of intersection of the circle with center P and radius p with the arc k or k'.

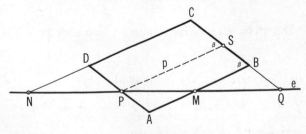

Figure 16

Now let us count the number of solutions. Observe that with any parallelogram $ABCD$ which solves the problem, we get a second solution by reflecting $ABCD$ in the line e. We shall agree *not* to consider two solutions different if they are just such mirror images of each other. To enumerate all the different solutions, it therefore suffices to count all the points of intersection on the arc k, since those on arc k' can be obtained by reflection.

For $\beta < 90°$ we have the following possibilities:

1) If $p > d$ [where $d = PQ/(\sin \beta)$ is twice the radius of the arc k] then the circle with center P and radius p does not intersect the arc k, and our problem has no solution.

2) If $p = d = PQ/(\sin \beta)$, then the circle with center P and radius p is tangent to k and the problem has exactly one solution (and, of course, its mirror image).

3) If $PQ < p < d = PQ/(\sin \beta)$, then the circle with center P and radius p intersects the arc k in two points, and our problem has two solutions (and, of course, their mirror images).

4) If $p < PQ$, then the circle with center P and radius p intersects k in one point, and the problem has one solution (and its mirror image); this is the situation pictured in Figure 15.

For $\beta \geq 90°$, there are only two possibilities:

1) If $p \geq PQ$, there is no solution.

2) If $p < PQ$, there is exactly one solution (and its reflection).

In the special case $\beta = 90°$, $ABCD$ is a rectangle and the arcs k and k' are semicircles with diameter PQ.

Once we have determined the point S, we may construct the parallelogram as follows: Draw a line through Q and S; the side BC will lie on this line. Draw a line parallel to QS through P; AD will lie on this line. Finally, draw lines parallel to PS through M and N. These, together with the pair of parallel lines previously constructed, will form the desired parallelogram.

1898 Competition

1898/1. Determine all positive integers n for which $2^n + 1$ is divisible by 3.

Solution. We start with the familiar identity

$$a^n - b^n = (a - b)(a^{n-1} + a^{n-2}b + \cdots + ab^{n-2} + b^{n-1}).$$

If we set $a = 2$ and $b = -1$, we obtain

$$2^n - (-1)^n = [2 - (-1)]A = 3A,$$

where A, the second factor on the right of the identity, is an integer since we substituted integers for a and b. Hence

$$2^n + 1 = 2^n - (-1)^n + 1 + (-1)^n = 3A + 1 + (-1)^n$$

which shows that $2^n + 1$ is divisible by 3 when n is odd, but gives a remainder of 2 when n is even.

Note 1. The notion of congruence. In order to formulate the essential part of the above solution, let us introduce a concept suggested by Gauss, the concept of congruence.

Definition: Let a, b, and m be three integers. We say that *a is congruent to b modulo m* and write

$$a \equiv b \pmod{m}$$

if the difference $a - b$ is divisible by m, that is, if there is an integer k such that

$$a - b = km;$$

m is called the *modulus*. Note that the integers a, b, m, k need not be positive; they may be negative, and a, b, and k may even be equal to zero. We may assume without loss of generality that m is positive, since the fact that an integer is divisible by m does not depend on the sign of m.

Examples:

$$2^2 \equiv 1, \quad 2^4 \equiv 1, \quad 2^6 \equiv 1, \quad \cdots \quad \pmod{3}$$

states that the numbers

$$2^2 - 1 = 3, \quad 2^4 - 1 = 15, \quad 2^6 - 1 = 63, \quad \cdots$$

are divisible by 3. The relation

$$a \equiv 0 \pmod{m}$$

says that a is divisible by m.

Let $m = 3$ and let us arrange the integers in increasing order by writing three consecutive numbers in one column, the next three in the next column, etc. Then we obtain the array

$$\cdots \quad -9 \quad -6 \quad -3 \quad 0 \quad 3 \quad 6 \quad 9 \quad \cdots$$
$$\cdots \quad -8 \quad -5 \quad -2 \quad 1 \quad 4 \quad 7 \quad 10 \quad \cdots$$
$$\cdots \quad -7 \quad -4 \quad -1 \quad 2 \quad 5 \quad 8 \quad 11 \quad \cdots.$$

It is easy to see that any two integers in the same row are congruent, and any two integers from different rows are not congruent.

Similarly, for an arbitrary modulus m, we can arrange the integers in an array consisting of m rows. This shows that, given any integer a, there is exactly one integer r among the numbers

$$0, \quad 1, \quad 2, \quad \cdots, \quad m - 1,$$

such that $r \equiv a \pmod{m}$. We shall call r the *remainder* of a with respect to m.

The following statements and theorems show that the concept of congruence resembles, in many respects, the concept of equality. A congruence is
reflexive: for every integer a, $a \equiv a \pmod{m}$;
symmetric: if $a \equiv b \pmod{m}$, then $b \equiv a \pmod{m}$;
transitive: if $a \equiv b \pmod{m}$ and $b \equiv c \pmod{m}$, then $a \equiv c \pmod{m}$.

THEOREM. *If $a \equiv a' \pmod{m}$ and $b \equiv b' \pmod{m}$, then*

$$a + b \equiv a' + b' \pmod{m}, \quad a - b \equiv a' - b' \pmod{m}, \quad ab \equiv a'b' \pmod{m}.$$

We shall prove the last statement in this theorem, the assertion about products, merely by using the definition of congruence. The expressions

$$a \equiv a' \pmod{m} \quad \text{and} \quad b \equiv b' \pmod{m}$$

say that there exist integers k and l such that

$$a = a' + km, \qquad b = b' + lm;$$

therefore

$$ab - a'b' = m(a'l + b'k + klm),$$

so that the difference $ab - a'b'$ is divisible by m, that is

$$ab \equiv a'b' \pmod{m}.$$

The following is a consequence of the above theorem: *If $a \equiv b \pmod{m}$, then $a^n \equiv b^n \pmod{m}$.*

Note 2. The last result may be used to solve our problem. The congruence

$$2 \equiv -1 \pmod{3}$$

implies that

$$2^n \equiv (-1)^n \pmod{3} \quad \text{or} \quad 2^n + 1 \equiv (-1)^n + 1 \pmod{3}.$$

Hence for odd n

$$2^n + 1 \equiv 0 \pmod{3},$$

that is, $2^n + 1$ is divisible by 3; and for even n,

$$2^n + 1 \equiv 2 \pmod{3},$$

that is, $2^n + 1$ is not divisible by 3.

1898/2. Prove the following theorem: If two triangles have a common angle, then the sum of the sines of the angles will be larger in that triangle where the difference of the remaining two angles is smaller.

On the basis of this theorem, determine the shape of that triangle for which the sum of the sines of its angles is a maximum.

Solution. a) Denote the angles of the triangles by α, β, γ and α', β',

γ', respectively and let $\alpha = \alpha'$. We first ask under what conditions the inequality

$$\sin \alpha + \sin \beta + \sin \gamma < \sin \alpha' + \sin \beta' + \sin \gamma'$$

or (equivalently, since $\alpha = \alpha'$)

$$(1) \qquad \sin \beta + \sin \gamma < \sin \beta' + \sin \gamma'$$

holds. This inequality can be written in the form

$$(2) \qquad 2 \sin \frac{\beta + \gamma}{2} \cos \frac{\beta - \gamma}{2} < 2 \sin \frac{\beta' + \gamma'}{2} \cos \frac{\beta' - \gamma'}{2}.$$

Since $\alpha = \alpha'$, we have $\beta + \gamma = \beta' + \gamma' < 180°$, so that

$$\sin \frac{\beta + \gamma}{2} = \sin \frac{\beta' + \gamma'}{2} > 0.$$

Dividing both sides of (2) by the positive number $\sin \frac{1}{2}(\beta + \gamma)$, we get

$$\cos \frac{\beta - \gamma}{2} < \cos \frac{\beta' - \gamma'}{2}.$$

This holds if and only if the absolute value of $\beta' - \gamma'$ is less than that of $\beta - \gamma$; that is, if and only if the difference between the angles β' and γ' is less than the difference between the angles β and γ.

b) According to a): If not all three angles of a triangle $\triangle$ are equal, say $\beta \neq \gamma$, then it is possible to find a triangle $\triangle'$ of different shape, such that the sum of the sines of the angles in $\triangle'$ is larger than the corresponding sum for $\triangle$. To construct $\triangle'$, take $\triangle$, leave its angle α unchanged, and replace β and γ by their arithmetic mean $\frac{1}{2}(\beta + \gamma)$. The angles of $\triangle'$ are $\alpha' = \alpha$, $\beta' = \gamma' = \frac{1}{2}(\beta + \gamma)$.

Thus, the sum of the sines of the angles in a non-equilateral triangle can always be increased in this manner. Therefore, only the equilateral triangle may maximize this sum.

Note. The existence of a maximum. Our previous considerations show that *if* there is a maximum among the sums of the sines of the angles in a triangle, then this maximum is attained only in an equilateral triangle. However, the existence of such a maximum is far from obvious. For, the sum of the sines in question may take on infinitely many values, and among infinitely many numbers there may not be a largest one.

The fact that a maximum exists in our case requires proof; we must show that the sum of the sines of the angles in an equilateral triangle $\triangle_E$ is greater than the corresponding sum in any other triangle $\triangle$.

1) If one angle of $\triangle$ is 60°, then $\triangle_E$ and $\triangle$ both have an angle of 60°.

The difference of the other two angles of $\triangle_E$ is zero, therefore of smaller absolute value than the corresponding difference for $\triangle$.

2) If $\triangle$ has no $60°$ angle, and if $\alpha \leq \beta \leq \gamma$, then clearly $\alpha < 60° < \gamma$, so that

$$60° - \alpha \quad \text{and} \quad \gamma - 60°$$

are *positive* numbers.

Draw a triangle $\triangle'$ with angles

$$\alpha' = 60°, \quad \beta' = \beta, \quad \text{hence} \quad \gamma' = \alpha + \gamma - 60°.$$

Then

$$\gamma' - \alpha' = (\alpha + \gamma - 60°) - 60° = (\gamma - 60°) - (60° - \alpha)$$

so that $|\gamma' - \alpha'|$ is the positive one of the two numbers

$$(\gamma - 60°) - (60° - \alpha) \quad \text{and} \quad (60° - \alpha) - (\gamma - 60°).$$

In either case

$$|\gamma' - \alpha'| < (\gamma - 60°) + (60° - \alpha) = \gamma - \alpha = |\gamma - \alpha|.$$

Now, since $\alpha' = 60°$, we know from 1) that the sum of the sines of the angles is smaller for $\triangle'$ than for $\triangle_E$. Moreover $\beta' = \beta$ and, as we just saw, the difference of the other two angles of $\triangle'$ is smaller in absolute value than the corresponding difference for $\triangle$. It follows from a), therefore, that the sum of the sines is smaller for the angles of $\triangle$ than for those of $\triangle'$; hence, it is also smaller than for those of $\triangle_E$.

1898/3. Let A, B, C, D be four given points on a straight line e. Construct a square such that two of its parallel sides (or their extensions) go through A and B respectively, and the other two sides (or their extensions) go through C and D, respectively.

Solution. We shall denote the length of a line segment XY also by XY. Let $PQRS$ (Figure 17) be a solution. If we rotate it about its center, a $90°$ turn carries CD into $C'D'$. Of course $C'D' \perp CD$ and $C'D' = CD$. But then there is a point B' with the following property: The segment BB' is perpendicular to the line e through C and D, has length CD, and B' is on the side PS through A.

Thus the construction is this: Through B we draw the perpendicular to the line through C and D and measure off $BB' = CD$. The sides of the square $PQRS$ will lie on the straight line AB', on the line through B parallel to AB', and on the lines through C and D perpendicular to AB'.

Since there are two segments BB' equal and perpendicular to CD, there are two solutions symmetrical with respect to the line e through C and D. Figure 17 shows only one of these squares.

Justification of the Solution. Through B draw the segment BL perpendicular to AB', and through C the segment CN perpendicular to DS; then in the right triangles BLB' and CND, $BB' = CD$ and $\angle LBB' = \angle NCD$ because the sides are pair-wise perpendicular. Consequently, these triangles are congruent. Therefore $BL = CN$, i.e. two adjacent sides of the constructed rectangle are equal.

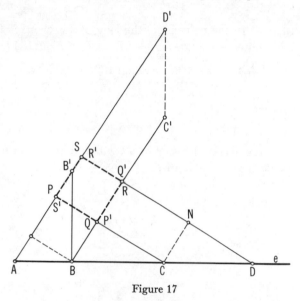

Figure 17

Remark. This construction is correct word for word whatever the position of the given points in the plane may be; see Figure 18.

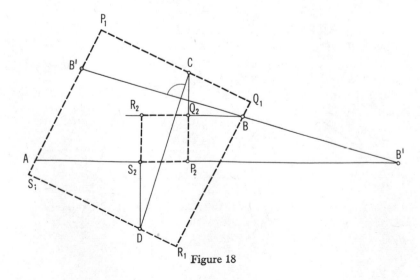

Figure 18

1899 Competition

1899/1. The points A_0, A_1, A_2, A_3, A_4 divide a unit circle (circle of radius 1) into five equal parts. Prove that the chords A_0A_1, A_0A_2 satisfy

$$(A_0A_1 \cdot A_0A_2)^2 = 5.$$

First Solution. In the unit circle, the length of a chord is twice the sine of half the subtended central angle. Thus (see Figures 19, 20)

$$A_0A_1 = 2 \sin 36° = 4 \sin 18° \cos 18°,$$

$$A_0A_2 = 2 \sin 72° = 2 \cos 18°,$$

and

$$A_0A_1 \cdot A_0A_2 = 8 \sin 18° \cos^2 18°.$$

But $2 \sin 18°$ is the length of a side of a regular 10-gon inscribed in the unit circle; this length, as we know, is $\frac{1}{2}(\sqrt{5} - 1)$. Hence

$$\sin 18° = \frac{\sqrt{5} - 1}{4},$$

$$\cos^2 18° = 1 - \sin^2 18° = 1 - \frac{6 - 2\sqrt{5}}{16}$$

$$= \frac{5 + \sqrt{5}}{8} = \sqrt{5} \frac{\sqrt{5} + 1}{8},$$

and

$$8 \sin 18° \cos^2 18° = \sqrt{5} \frac{5 - 1}{4} = \sqrt{5}.$$

Therefore, in fact,

$$(A_0A_1 \cdot A_0A_2)^2 = (\sqrt{5})^2 = 5.$$

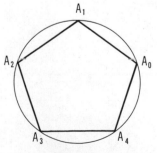

Figure 19

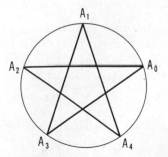

Figure 20

Note. Regular polygons. In our problem A_0A_1 is a side of the 5-gon in Figure 19 (the sides intersect only at the vertices), A_0A_2 is a side of the 5-gon in Figure 20. Both figures show regular polygons because, by definition, every figure constructed as follows is a regular polygon: We start at some point A_0 of the circumference of a circle and measure off a chord a so chosen that, after measuring it off n times consecutively (following the circle in the same sense), we come again to A_0 and all n vertices are distinct.

For a given n we get all possible inscribed regular n-gons if we choose a as the chord subtending the arc

$$\frac{k}{n}\,360°,$$

taking for k, one after the other, all positive integers less than $n/2$ and prime to n. If k is not prime to n, the construction described above leads us back to A_0 too soon; for example, $n = 10$, $k = 4$ gives a regular polygon with only 5 instead of 10 vertices.

For $k = 1$, we get a regular polygon whose sides meet only at their end points.

For $k > 1$, we get a regular polygon whose sides intersect also at other points.

If n is an odd prime p, k may take on *all* integral values from 1 to $\frac{1}{2}(p-1)$; so in this case there are $\frac{1}{2}(p-1)$ different inscribed regular p-gons.

If n is a composite number, there are fewer than $\frac{1}{2}(n-1)$ different regular n-gons; thus, if $n = 24$, there are only four.

Second Solution. In the following solution our knowledge of regular polygons is not used.

The lengths of the segments A_0A_1, A_0A_2 are connected in a simple way with the cosines of those angles φ for which 5φ is an odd multiple of $90°$, that is, those for which

$$\cos 5\varphi = 0.$$

We may restrict our attention to φ-values from 0 to $180°$ since, for values greater than $180°$, we can always find an angle between 0 and $180°$ with the same cosine. With this restriction, the cosines are:

$$\cos\left(\tfrac{1}{5}\cdot 90°\right) = \cos\ 18° = \sin\ 72° = \tfrac{1}{2}A_0A_2,$$

$$\cos\left(\tfrac{3}{5}\cdot 90°\right) = \cos\ 54° = \sin\ 36° = \tfrac{1}{2}A_0A_1,$$

$$\cos\left(\tfrac{5}{5}\cdot 90°\right) = \cos\ 90° = 0,$$

$$\cos\left(\tfrac{7}{5}\cdot 90°\right) = \cos 126° = -\sin\ 36° = -\tfrac{1}{2}A_0A_1,$$

$$\cos\left(\tfrac{9}{5}\cdot 90°\right) = \cos 162° = -\sin\ 72° = -\tfrac{1}{2}A_0A_2.$$

We shall rewrite the equation $\cos 5\varphi = 0$ as a polynomial equation in cos φ (which we shall denote by x); the above expressions will be roots of this equation, and the value of $(A_0A_1 \cdot A_0A_2)^2$ can then be found easily.

To this end we shall express

$$\cos n\varphi \quad \text{and} \quad \frac{\sin (n + 1)\varphi}{\sin \varphi}$$

recursively for $n = 0, 1, 2, 3, 4, 5$ in terms of $x = \cos \varphi$. [We use $\sin (n + 1)\varphi/\sin \varphi$ instead of $\sin (n + 1)\varphi$ in order to obtain expressions free of square roots.]

The expressions $T_n(x)$, $U_n(x)$ we find for $\cos n\varphi$, $\sin (n + 1)\varphi/\sin \varphi$, respectively, in terms of $x = \cos \varphi$ are obtained as follows:

$$\cos 0 = T_0(x) = 1, \qquad \frac{\sin \varphi}{\sin \varphi} = U_0(x) = 1,$$

$$\cos \varphi = T_1(x) = x, \qquad \frac{\sin 2\varphi}{\sin \varphi} = 2 \cos \varphi = U_1(x) = 2x.$$

In general, we shall use the recursion identity

$$\cos (n + 1)\varphi = \cos \varphi \cos n\varphi - \sin \varphi \sin n\varphi$$

$$= \cos \varphi \cos n\varphi - (1 - \cos^2 \varphi) \frac{\sin n\varphi}{\sin \varphi},$$

that is,

(1) $$T_{n+1}(x) = xT_n(x) - (1 - x^2)U_{n-1}(x);$$

and the recursion identity

$$\frac{\sin (n + 2)\varphi}{\sin \varphi} = \frac{1}{\sin \varphi} [\sin \varphi \cos (n + 1)\varphi + \cos \varphi \sin (n + 1)\varphi],$$

that is

(2) $$U_{n+1}(x) = T_{n+1}(x) + xU_n(x).$$

Alternate application of (1) and (2) gives

$$T_2(x) = xT_1(x) - (1 - x^2)U_0(x) = x \cdot x - (1 - x^2) = 2x^2 - 1$$

$$U_2(x) = T_2(x) + xU_1(x) = 2x^2 - 1 + x \cdot 2x = 4x^2 - 1$$

$$T_3(x) = x(2x^2 - 1) - (1 - x^2) \cdot 2x = 4x^3 - 3x$$

$$U_3(x) = 4x^3 - 3x + x(4x^2 - 1) = 8x^3 - 4x$$

$$T_4(x) = x(4x^3 - 3x) - (1 - x^2)(4x^2 - 1) = 8x^4 - 8x^2 + 1$$

$$U_4(x) = 8x^4 - 8x^2 + 1 + x(8x^3 - 4x) = 16x^4 - 12x^2 + 1$$

and

$$T_5(x) = x(8x^4 - 8x^2 + 1) - (1 - x^2)(8x^3 - 4x)$$
$$= x(8x^4 - 8x^2 + 1 + 8x^4 - 12x^2 + 4)$$
$$= x(16x^4 - 20x^2 + 5) = x[(2x)^4 - 5(2x)^2 + 5].$$

In our notation, $T_5(x) = \cos 5\varphi$, where φ is an angle such that $\cos 5\varphi = 0$. Therefore, the roots of $T_5(x) = 0$ are just the five cosines

$$\tfrac{1}{2}A_0A_1, \quad -\tfrac{1}{2}A_0A_1, \quad 0, \quad \tfrac{1}{2}A_0A_2, \quad -\tfrac{1}{2}A_0A_2$$

evaluated earlier. If from $T_5(x)$, we take out the factor x corresponding to the root 0, and if we set

$$(2x)^2 = u,$$

we get the quadratic equation

$$u^2 - 5u + 5 = 0;$$

its roots are just $(A_0A_1)^2$ and $(A_0A_2)^2$. Since the product of the roots is the constant term, it follows that

$$(A_0A_1 \cdot A_0A_2)^2 = 5.$$

Note 1. Generalization of the theorem proved above. Chebyshev polynomials. The theorem just proved is a particularly simple instance of the following:

If $n = p^k$, where p is a prime and k a positive integer, and if the different regular n-gons inscribable in the unit circle have side lengths $a_1, a_2, \cdots, a_t$, then

$$(a_1 \cdot a_2 \cdots a_t)^2 = p.$$

Figure 21

Figure 22

For example, for $n = 2^3$, the sides of the regular inscribed 8-gons (Figures 21, 22) have lengths

$$a_1 = 2 \sin \frac{45°}{2} \quad \text{and} \quad a_2 = 2 \sin \frac{135°}{2} = 2 \cos \frac{45°}{2}.$$

The product $a_1 a_2$ is

$$4 \sin \frac{45°}{2} \cos \frac{45°}{2} = 2 \sin 45° = \sqrt{2},$$

and

$$(a_1 a_2)^2 = 2.$$

A proof of the general theorem involves a closer examination of the equations

$$T_1(x) = 0, \quad U_1(x) = 0, \quad T_2(x) = 0, \quad U_2(x) = 0, \quad \cdots.$$

The polynomials $T_n(x)$ and $U_n(x)$ which express

$$\cos n\varphi \quad \text{and} \quad \frac{\sin (n+1)\varphi}{\sin \varphi}$$

as functions of $x = \cos\varphi$ are called *Chebyshev polynomials.*†

Note 2. A geometric application of complex numbers. The following holds for regular polygons with any number of sides:

If A_0, A_1, $\cdots$, A_{n-1} are the vertices of a regular n-gon inscribed in the unit circle, then

$$A_0 A_1 \cdot A_0 A_2 \cdots A_0 A_{n-1} = n.$$

We give a simple proof for those acquainted with complex numbers.‡

We represent the regular n-gon in the complex plane, drawing the unit circle about the origin and placing the vertex A_0 at the point 1 on the real axis (see Figure 23). If we denote the nearest vertex (going from A_0 in the counter clockwise direction) by the complex number ϵ, then the vertices of the n-gon correspond to the complex numbers

$$1, \quad \epsilon, \quad \epsilon^2, \quad \cdots, \quad \epsilon^{n-1};$$

each has absolute value 1, and their amplitudes are

$$0, \quad \frac{360°}{n}, \quad 2\frac{360°}{n}, \quad \cdots, \quad (n-1)\frac{360°}{n},$$

respectively.

---

† P. L. Chebyshev, a Russian mathematician, was born in 1821 near Moscow; he died in 1894 in St. Petersburg, where he was a professor at the university. He proved the following oft-quoted theorem of number theory: *If $x \geq 1$, then there is a prime p for which $x < p \leq 2x$.* For example, if $x = 1$, then $1 < 2 \leq 2$; if $x = 10$, then $10 < 11, 13, 17, 19 < 20$.

‡ For some basic concepts concerning complex numbers, see for example K. Knopp, *Elements of the Theory of Functions*, New York, Dover Publications, Inc., 1952.

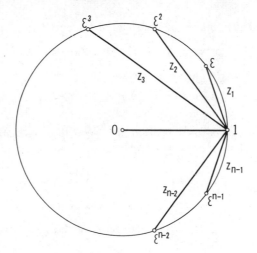

Figure 23

The lengths of the segments from A_0 to the other vertices correspond to the absolute values of the complex numbers $1 - \epsilon$, $1 - \epsilon^2$, $\cdots$, $1 - \epsilon^{n-1}$, so that the theorem, in terms of complex numbers, states

(1) $$| (1 - \epsilon)(1 - \epsilon^2) \cdots (1 - \epsilon^{n-1}) | = n.$$

To prove this, we note that

$$\epsilon^n = 1$$

and, in general, for integers k,

$$(\epsilon^k)^n = (\epsilon^n)^k = 1.$$

Thus $1, \epsilon, \epsilon^2, \cdots, \epsilon^{n-1}$ are the zeros of the polynomial

$$z^n - 1 = (z - 1)(z^{n-1} + z^{n-2} + \cdots + z + 1).$$

Since the first factor on the right vanishes only at $z = 1$, the numbers

$$\epsilon, \quad \epsilon^2, \quad \cdots, \quad \epsilon^{n-1}$$

are the zeros of the polynomial

$$f(z) = z^{n-1} + z^{n-2} + \cdots + z + 1.$$

Therefore, $f(z)$ factors into

$$f(z) = (z - \epsilon)(z - \epsilon^2) \cdots (z - \epsilon^{n-1}).$$

If we substitute 1 for z, we obtain

$$f(1) = (1 - \epsilon)(1 - \epsilon^2) \cdots (1 - \epsilon^{n-1}) = n.$$

This is more than (1) claims: not only the absolute value of the product, but the product itself is n.

1899/2. Let x_1 and x_2 be the roots of the equation

$$x^2 - (a + d)x + ad - bc = 0.$$

Show that x_1^3 and x_2^3 are the roots of

$$y^2 - (a^3 + d^3 + 3abc + 3bcd)y + (ad - bc)^3 = 0.$$

Solution. By known relations between the roots and coefficients of second degree equations, the fact that x_1, x_2 are roots of

$$x^2 - (a + d)x + ad - bc = 0$$

implies that

$$a + d = x_1 + x_2, \qquad ad - bc = x_1 x_2.$$

We use these to express the coefficients of the second equation in terms of x_1 and x_2:

$$a^3 + d^3 + 3abc + 3bcd = a^3 + d^3 + 3(a + d)bc$$
$$= (a + d)^3 - 3(a + d)(ad - bc)$$
$$= (x_1 + x_2)^3 - 3(x_1 + x_2)x_1 x_2$$
$$= x_1^3 + x_2^3$$

and

$$(ad - bc)^3 = x_1^3 x_2^3.$$

Therefore, the equation

$$y^2 - (a^3 + d^3 + 3abc + 3bcd)y + (ad - bc)^3 = 0$$

is equivalent to

$$y^2 - (x_1^3 + x_2^3)y + x_1^3 x_2^3 = 0,$$

and this factors into

$$(y - x_1^3)(y - x_2^3) = 0.$$

Thus its roots are indeed x_1^3 and x_2^3.

Note. On reducing irrational equations. Denote $a + d$ by p and $ad - bc$ by q; then the problem answers the following question:

If the cube root of a number y satisfies

$$x^2 + px + q = 0,$$

does y also satisfy an equation in integral powers of y, and if so, how is this equation found? In short, can

$$(1) \qquad (\sqrt[3]{y})^2 + p\sqrt[3]{y} + q = 0$$

be reduced to an equation in which no fractional powers of y appear, and if so, how? In the above problem the desired equation was given and merely had to be verified. However, one can derive the equation and this derivation will show how, in general, one can eliminate radicals from an equation.†

First, multiply equation

(1) $$(\sqrt[3]{y})^2 + p\sqrt[3]{y} + q = 0$$

by $\sqrt[3]{y}$, obtaining

(2) $$p(\sqrt[3]{y})^2 + q\sqrt[3]{y} + y = 0.$$

Next, multiply this result by $\sqrt[3]{y}$:

(3) $$q(\sqrt[3]{y})^2 + y\sqrt[3]{y} + py = 0.$$

Eliminate $(\sqrt[3]{y})^2$ from equations (1) and (2), then from (1) and (3). This gives

$$(q - p^2)\sqrt[3]{y} + y - pq = 0$$
$$(y - qp)\sqrt[3]{y} + py - q^2 = 0.$$

Then, eliminate $\sqrt[3]{y}$ from these two to get

$$(py - q^2)(q - p^2) - (y - pq)^2 = 0,$$

which is the same as

$$y^2 + (p^3 - 3pq)y + q^3 = 0.$$

If we substitute the values of p and q into the last equation, we obtain the polynomial of the original problem.

In this procedure it was inessential that the radical sign stood over the unknown y alone; one could just as well have had a kth root, $\sqrt[k]{\ }$, of a more complicated expression in which the unknown is combined with constants by means of the operations $+, -, \times, \div$. Nor need k be 3. To handle the more general case, we multiply the given equation repeatedly by the radical to be eliminated until we have the right number of equations in order to eliminate every power of that radical. This number is finite, since only the first $k - 1$ powers of the radical can occur.‡ Then, all we have to do is to eliminate successive powers of the radical and thus eliminate it entirely.

---

† It is to be understood that we deal here with polynomial equations $Q(x) = 0$ having rational coefficients, i.e., with algebraic equations, but that the unknown may appear in irrational form; the same question might be formulated also as follows:

If $\sqrt[k]{r_1}$, $\sqrt[k]{r_2}$ are roots of $Q(x) = 0$, construct an equation $Q'(x) = 0$ with roots r_1 and r_2.

‡ Any power greater than $k - 1$ of the radical can be reduced to a power less than or equal to $k - 1$ by means of the relation

$$(\sqrt[k]{Y})^k = Y.$$

For example,

$$(\sqrt[k]{Y})^{k+2} = Y(\sqrt[k]{Y})^2.$$

Should there be several radicals, possibly with different exponents, the process is to be repeated for each, until no radical sign stands over an expression involving the unknown.

This plausibility argument shows: *An equation containing the unknown in irrational form is reducible to one in which only integral powers of the unknown occur*, no matter how many radicals the original equation contains and to *what* powers. We shall not consider the details of the proof.

Though a method of constructing the desired equation has been outlined, it is to be noted that, as the number of radicals and their powers increase, the calculations become quite difficult.

1899/3. Prove that, for any natural number n, the expression

$$A = 2903^n - 803^n - 464^n + 261^n$$

is divisible by 1897.

Solution. By virtue of the well-known identity

$$a^n - b^n = (a - b)(a^{n-1} + a^{n-2}b + \cdots + ab^{n-2} + b^{n-1}),$$

the difference of the nth powers of two integers is divisible by the difference of the integers themselves.

The number A equals

$$2903^n - 464^n - (803^n - 261^n),$$

and $2903^n - 464^n$ is divisible by

$$2903 - 464 = 2439 = 9 \cdot 271,$$

while $803^n - 261^n$ is divisible by

$$803 - 261 = 542 = 2 \cdot 271,$$

so that A is divisible by 271; that is $A = 271B$, where B is an integer.

But A is also equal to

$$2903^n - 803^n - (464^n - 261^n),$$

where $2903^n - 803^n$ is divisible by

$$2903 - 803 = 2100 = 7 \cdot 300,$$

and $464^n - 261^n$ is divisible by

$$464 - 261 = 203 = 7 \cdot 29,$$

so that A is also divisible by 7.

Since 271 is not divisible by the prime 7, $A = 271B$ is divisible by 7 only if B is [see part a) of the Note to the Second Solution of 1894/1]. Hence, $B = 7C$, where C is an integer, so that $A = 271 \cdot 7C = 1897C$ is indeed divisible by 1897.

1900 Competition

1900/1. Let a, b, c, d, be fixed integers with d not divisible by 5. Assume that m is an integer for which

$$am^3 + bm^2 + cm + d$$

is divisible by 5. Prove that there exists an integer n for which

$$dn^3 + cn^2 + bn + a$$

is also divisible by 5.

Solution. The integer m is not divisible by 5. For, otherwise,

$$am^3 + bm^2 + cm + d = m(am^2 + bm + c) + d$$

would be divisible by 5 only if d were divisible by 5, contrary to the assumption.

The number m, therefore, is of the form

$$m = 5k + r$$

where k is an integer and r a positive integer less than 5.

For the sake of brevity, let us set

$$A = am^3 + bm^2 + cm + d,$$

$$B = dn^3 + cn^2 + bn + a.$$

If we eliminate d from these expressions, we get

$$An^3 - B = a(m^3n^3 - 1) + bn(m^2n^2 - 1) + cn^2(mn - 1)$$

$$= (mn - 1)[a(m^2n^2 + mn + 1) + bn(mn + 1) + cn^2].$$

Now, if $m = 5k + r$ is a number such that A is divisible by 5, and if we can choose n so that the right side of the last identity is divisible by 5, then B will be divisible by 5. We shall achieve this by choosing, for every m not divisible by 5, an integer n so that the factor $(mn - 1)$ on the right is divisible by 5. In particular, since $m = 5k + r$, $mn = 5kn + rn$, so that $mn - 1$ is divisible by 5 whenever rn is 1 plus a multiple of 5. So, if $r = 1$, choose $n = 1$; if $r = 2$, choose $n = 3$; if $r = 3$, choose $n = 2$; and if $r = 4$, choose $n = 4$. In this way, for every m, we have found an n which makes $mn - 1$ divisible by 5, and hence, for which B is divisible by 5.

1900/2. Construct a triangle ABC, given the length c of its side AB, the radius r of its inscribed circle, and the radius r_c of its ex-circle tangent to the side AB and to the extensions of BC and CA.

Solution. a) Let D be the point of tangency of the inscribed circle k to the side BC; let D' be the point of tangency of the other circle k' to the extension of BC. (See Figure 24.)

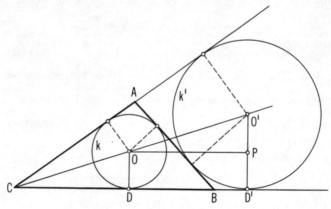

Figure 24

We know [cf. 1896/3, Note 2, (1) and (2)] that, if a, b, c are the lengths of the sides and $2s$ the perimeter of the triangle,

$$CD = s - c, \qquad CD' = s,$$

so that

$$DD' = s - (s - c) = c.$$

b) From the fact that the circles k and k' (with centers O and O' respectively) do not intersect, we shall derive a relation between r, r_c and c. To this end, draw a line through O parallel to BC, intersecting $O'D'$ in P; $\triangle OPO'$ is a right triangle with sides $OP = DD' = c$, $O'P = r_c - r$, and hypotenuse $OO' \geq r_c + r$. By Pythagoras' theorem,

$$(OO')^2 = c^2 + (r_c - r)^2 \geq (r_c + r)^2,$$

that is

$$c^2 + r_c^2 - 2r_c r + r^2 \geq r_c^2 + 2r_c r + r^2,$$

or

(1)
$$\frac{c^2}{2} \geq rr_c.†$$

c) If the given data c, r, and r_c obey condition (1), and if $r_c > r$, then $\triangle ABC$ may be constructed as follows: Draw a segment DD' of length c, and draw perpendicular segments OD, $O'D'$ of lengths r, r_c at D, D', respectively. Draw the circle k of radius r about O, and the circle k' of radius r_c about O'. Since $r_c > r$, the line through O and O' intersects the line through D and D'. Their point of intersection is the vertex C of the desired $\triangle ABC$, since C is the only point on $D'D$ from which two common outer tangents can be drawn to both circles.

The circles k and k' do not intersect, because condition (1) implies

$$(OO')^2 = c^2 + (r_c - r)^2 = (r_c + r)^2 + c^2 - 4rr_c \geq (r_c + r)^2.$$

Next, draw one of the inner tangents common to both circles. It will intersect the outer tangents from C in the desired vertices A and B of $\triangle ABC$ because, by the reasoning in a), $AB = DD' = c$. (The other inner tangent yields another solution congruent to the first. If k and k' are tangent, there is only one solution.)

1900/3. A cliff is 300 meters high. Consider two free-falling raindrops such that the second one leaves the top of the cliff when the first one has already fallen .001 millimeters. What is the distance between the drops at the moment the first hits the ground? (Compute the answer to within .1 mm. Neglect air resistance, etc.)

Solution. Let σ be the distance the first drop has fallen at the instant the second drop leaves the cliff, and let τ be the time needed for this descent of σ. Let s be the total height of the cliff and t the time needed for a raindrop to fall this entire distance. Let s' be the distance the second drop falls from the time it leaves the cliff to the time the first hits the ground, that is, in the interval $t - \tau$. We wish to compute $s - s'$.

Then, by the law governing the free fall of bodies under the influence of gravity, we have

$$\sigma = \tfrac{1}{2}g\tau^2, \quad s = \tfrac{1}{2}gt^2, \quad \text{and} \quad s' = \tfrac{1}{2}g(t - \tau)^2.$$

Hence,

$$\tau = \sqrt{\frac{2\sigma}{g}}, \qquad t = \sqrt{\frac{2s}{g}},$$

† This much of the solution answers also 1927/3.

so that

$$s' = \frac{g}{2}\left(\sqrt{\frac{2s}{g}} - \sqrt{\frac{2\sigma}{g}}\right)^2 = s - 2\sqrt{\sigma s} + \sigma$$

and

$$s - s' = 2\sqrt{s\sigma} - \sigma.$$

In our problem, $\sigma = .001$ mm., $s = 300\ 000$ mm., so that

$$s - s' = 2\sqrt{300} - .001 \sim 34.6 \text{ mm.}$$

1901 Competition

1901/1. Prove that, for any positive integer n,

$$1^n + 2^n + 3^n + 4^n$$

is divisible by 5 if and only if n is not divisible by 4.

First Solution. Each of the numbers

$$1^4 = 1, \qquad 2^4 = 16 = 5 \cdot 3 + 1, \qquad 3^4 = 81 = 5 \cdot 16 + 1, \qquad 4^4 = 256 = 5 \cdot 51 + 1$$

is of the form $5k + 1$, where k is an integer. Moreover, if A stands for any of the numbers 1, 2, 3 or 4, and if l is a positive integer, then A^{4l} is of the form $5k + 1$ because (cf. identity used in 1898/1)

$$A^{4l} - 1 = (A^4)^l - 1 = (A^4 - 1)[(A^4)^{l-1} + (A^4)^{l-2} + \cdots + 1],$$

where the first factor on the right is divisible by 5 and the second is an integer.

Any positive integer may be written in the form $4l + r$ where l is a positive integer or zero, and the remainder r is one of the numbers 0, 1, 2, or 3. In particular, our exponent n may be written in this form so that

$$
\begin{aligned}
S &= 1^n + 2^n + 3^n + 4^n \\
&= 1 + 2^{4l+r} + 3^{4l+r} + 4^{4l+r} \\
&= 1 + 2^{4l}2^r + 3^{4l}3^r + 4^{4l}4^r \\
&= 1 + (5k_1 + 1)2^r + (5k_2 + 1)3^r + (5k_3 + 1)4^r \\
&= 5(k_1 2^r + k_2 3^r + k_3 4^r) + (1 + 2^r + 3^r + 4^r) \\
&= 5m + R,
\end{aligned}
$$

where m is an integer, and

$$R = 1 + 2^r + 3^r + 4^r.$$

Thus, S is divisible by 5 if and only if R is. If n is divisible by 4, then $r = 0$ and $R = 4$; in this case S is not divisible by 5. But if n is not divisible by 4, then $r = 1$, 2 or 3, and the corresponding values of R are 10, 30 or 100; in this case S is divisible by 5.

Second Solution. Observe (cf. Note 1 to 1898/1) that

$$1^4 = \ 1 \equiv 1 \ (\text{mod } 5), \qquad 2^4 = \ 16 \equiv 1 \ (\text{mod } 5),$$

$$3^4 = 81 \equiv 1 \ (\text{mod } 5), \qquad 4^4 = 256 \equiv 1 \ (\text{mod } 5).$$

Let $n = 4k + r$, where k is an integer and r is 0, 1, 2 or 3. If a is 1, 2, 3 or 4,

$$a^4 \equiv 1 \ (\text{mod } 5), \quad \text{hence} \quad a^{4k} \equiv 1 \ (\text{mod } 5).$$

Thus

$$a^n = a^{4k}a^r \equiv a^r \ (\text{mod } 5),$$

and by the theorem on congruences (cf. Note 1 to 1898/1)

$$S = 1^n + 2^n + 3^n + 4^n \equiv 1^r + 2^r + 3^r + 4^r \ (\text{mod } 5).$$

It follows that

$$\text{if} \quad r = 0, \quad S \equiv \ \ 4 \equiv 4 \ (\text{mod } 5);$$

$$\text{if} \quad r = 1, \quad S \equiv \ 10 \equiv 0 \ (\text{mod } 5);$$

$$\text{if} \quad r = 2, \quad S \equiv \ 30 \equiv 0 \ (\text{mod } 5);$$

$$\text{if} \quad r = 3, \quad S \equiv 100 \equiv 0 \ (\text{mod } 5);$$

so that S is indeed divisible by 5 if and only if n is not divisible by 4.

Note. Fermat's theorem. Our solution is based on the fact that

$$1^4 \equiv 2^4 \equiv 3^4 \equiv 4^4 \equiv 1 \ (\text{mod } 5).$$

This congruence is a special case of the following theorem due to Fermat:[†]

If a is an integer not divisible by the prime p, then

$$a^{p-1} \equiv 1 \ (\text{mod } p).$$

† The French mathematician P. Fermat was born in 1601 and died in 1665, a member of the Toulouse parliament. He proved many beautiful number theoretical results, among them the one stated here. Following the custom of his time, he published his results without proof. Later mathematicians endeavored to prove his theorems and in the course of their efforts, contributed much to number theory. Fermat also played a part in the founding of analytic geometry.

Fermat's Theorem, stated here, should not be confused with the famous conjecture known as "Fermat's Last Theorem", which says that no non-zero integral values of x, y, z exist that satisfy the equation $x^n + y^n = z^n$ if n is an integer greater than 2; see 1909/1, Note.

To prove this, consider the set of all permutations of m things, p at a time, with repetitions allowed. Classify these m^p permutations by putting into one class all those that can be obtained from each other by cyclic permutations (cf. 1895/1, Note 1). The number of elements in any one class is a divisor of p (as we showed in Note 1 to 1895/1), and hence is either 1 or p. We shall show that there are precisely m classes with one element each, and so the remaining permutations fall into classes of p elements each.

An arrangement consisting of a p-fold repetition of the same object is in a class by itself because a cyclic permutation (which replaces every object by its left neighbor, and the first by the last) just yields the same element back again. Since there are m objects, there are m different p-fold repetitions of one object; hence there are m classes each containing one such permutation.

Each of the remaining $m^p - m$ permutations contains at least two distinct objects, and a cyclic permutation of such an arrangement yields a new permutation. Consequently, these $m^p - m$ permutations must fall into classes containing p elements each.

Thus $m^p - m$ is p times the number of these classes, that is,

$$m^p - m \equiv 0 \pmod{p}.$$

It follows that

$$m(m^p - 1) \equiv 0 \pmod{p}.$$

This proves Fermat's theorem for any positive integer m, since the last congruence implies that, if m is not divisible by p, then $m^p - 1$ is. (Cf. Note to Second Solution of 1894/1.)

To prove the theorem for any integer a, choose a positive integer m congruent to $a \pmod{p}$. It is easy to show that Fermat's theorem for m implies it for a.†

1901/2. If

$$u = \cot 22°30', \quad v = \frac{1}{\sin 22°30'},$$

prove that u satisfies a quadratic and v a quartic (4th degree) equation with integral coefficients and with leading coefficients 1.

---

† There are many ways of proving Fermat's theorem. Two proofs by Euler were the first to appear in print. An earlier proof by Leibniz appeared only in 1863 in his collected works. Gauss found, independently, a proof similar to that of Leibniz. The proof given here is based on those due to Gauss and Leibniz.

G. W. Leibniz, philosopher, mathematician, and diplomat, was born in Leipzig in 1646 and died in Hannover in 1716. He invented the differential and integral calculus at the same time as Newton did.

Solution. We first construct an angle of 22°30′, that is one-fourth of a right angle. This may be done as follows (see Figure 25): Let ABC be an isosceles right triangle with $CA = BC$, extend the side CA to a point D such that $AD = AB$; draw the segment BD. The angle at D of the isosceles triangle DAB is half the angle CAB, which in turn is 45°. So, $\sphericalangle ADB = 22°30′$.

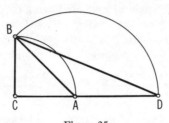

Figure 25

If we choose AC as the unit length, then

$$DA = AB = \sqrt{AC^2 + BC^2} = \sqrt{2}, \qquad DC = DA + AC = \sqrt{2} + 1,$$

and

$$DB = \sqrt{DC^2 + BC^2} = \sqrt{(\sqrt{2} + 1)^2 + 1} = \sqrt{4 + 2\sqrt{2}}.$$

The values of u and v are:

$$u = \cot 22°30′ = \frac{DC}{BC} = \sqrt{2} + 1,$$

$$v = \frac{1}{\sin 22°30′} = \frac{DB}{BC} = \sqrt{4 + 2\sqrt{2}},$$

so that

$$(u - 1)^2 = 2, \quad v^2 = 4 + 2\sqrt{2}, \quad (v^2 - 4)^2 = 8.$$

These give

$$u^2 - 2u - 1 = 0 \quad \text{and} \quad v^4 - 8v^2 + 8 = 0.$$

Note. Algebraic and transcendental numbers. Algebraic integers. If a number α satisfies an algebraic equation

$$x^n + a_1 x^{n-1} + \cdots + a_n = 0$$

with rational coefficients $a_1, a_2, \cdots, a_n$, then α is called an *algebraic number*.

Every rational number r is algebraic since it satisfies the algebraic equation with rational coefficients $x - r = 0$. However, not every algebraic number is rational; for example, $\sqrt{2}$ is an algebraic number because it satisfies the equation $x^2 - 2 = 0$, yet it is irrational.

Not every number is algebraic. Those real or complex numbers which are not algebraic are called *transcendental numbers*.† Among the well-known numbers, e (the base of natural logarithms) and π are examples of transcendental numbers. The first proof of the transcendence of e is due to Hermite‡ (1873); that of the transcendence of π is due to Lindemann§ (1882). (It is a consequence of the transcendence of π that it is impossible to construct, with straightedge and compass alone, a line segment equal in length to the circumference of a given circle, or a square having the area of a given circle.)

Among algebraic numbers, we distinguish algebraic integers: A number α is said to be an *algebraic integer* if it satisfies an algebraic equation with integral coefficients and leading coefficient 1. For example,

$$\alpha_1 = \frac{-1 + \sqrt{5}}{2}, \qquad \alpha_2 = \frac{-1 - \sqrt{5}}{2}$$

are algebraic integers in spite of their fractional form, because they are roots of the quadratic equation

$$x^2 + x - 1 = 0$$

with integral coefficients and leading coefficient 1. It can be shown that the sum, difference, product and quotient (with a non-zero divisor) of two algebraic numbers are algebraic numbers, and that the sum, difference and product of two algebraic integers are algebraic integers.

Our problem was to prove that the cotangent and the reciprocal of the sine of $90°/4$ are algebraic integers.

1901/3. Let a and b be two natural numbers whose greatest common divisor (g.c.d.) is d:

$$(a, b) = d.\P$$

Prove that exactly d of the numbers

$$a, \ 2a, \ 3a, \ \cdots, \ (b-1)a, \ ba$$

are divisible by b.

---

† For simple expositions of the two classical proofs of the existence of transcendental numbers, see I. Niven, *Numbers: Rational and Irrational* in this series.

‡ Hermite was born in 1822 and died in 1901 in Paris, where he was a professor at the *École Polytechnique* and at the University. He was president of the *Académie des Sciences*. As the most outstanding mathematician of his time, he was a member of many scientific societies.

§ F. Lindemann was born in 1852 and died in Hannover in 1939; he was a professor at the University of Munich.

¶ The symbol (x, y) means "g.c.d. of x and y"; see Note 2 for a precise definition of g.c.d.

Solution. We have

$$a = dr, \qquad b = ds;$$

hence [see Note 3, theorem (i)]

$$(r, s) = 1.†$$

If we divide $a, 2a, \cdots, (b-1)a, ba$ by b, we obtain the quotients

$$\frac{r}{s}, \quad \frac{2r}{s}, \quad \cdots, \quad \frac{(b-1)r}{s}, \quad \frac{(ds)r}{s}.$$

Since r and s are relatively prime, the only integers here are the quotients in which the coefficient of r in the numerator is a multiple of s; see Note 3, theorem (ii). Since $b = ds$, this happens d times as the coefficients go through the values $1, 2, \cdots, ds$.

Note 1. The divisors of a positive integer. It is easy to find the divisors of a positive integer if we can write it as a power product of primes (cf. Note to 1896/1). If

$$a = vp^{\alpha}, \qquad b = wp^{\beta},$$

where v and w are not divisible by the prime p, then the product ab contains p to the power $\alpha + \beta$. (This becomes evident when the multiplication is carried out.)

It follows that a positive number a is divisible by b if and only if b contains no prime to an exponent higher than the corresponding exponent in the prime power product for a.

For example, the number $a = 2^m p$, where p is an odd prime, has the following divisors:

$$1, \quad 2, \quad 2^2, \quad \cdots, \quad 2^{m-1}, \quad 2^m,$$

$$p, \quad 2p, \quad 2^2 p, \quad \cdots, \quad 2^{m-1} p, \quad 2^m p.$$

Note 2. The greatest common divisor. If the integers $a, b, \cdots, m$ are not all zero, they have a finite number of common divisors. The largest of these is always *positive* and is called their *greatest common divisor*; it is often denoted by $(a, b, \cdots, m)$.

Since zero is divisible by every number, the greatest common divisor of any set of integers is equal to that of the non-zero integers among them. Moreover, negative numbers may be replaced by their absolute values. Hence, for *any* set of integers, finding the g.c.d. is reduced to finding that of a set of positive integers.

From Note 1 we know that *if $a, b, \cdots, m$ are positive integers and if d is their g.c.d., then the power of a given prime in the prime power product for d is*

---

† If the g.c.d. of two numbers is 1, they are called "relatively prime"; see Note 3.

the smallest that occurs in the prime power products for a, b, $\cdots$, and m for that prime.

For example

$$(2^5 \cdot 3^{24} \cdot 7^9 \cdot 11^{15}, \quad 2^9 \cdot 3^{10} \cdot 13^8) = 2^5 \cdot 3^{10}.$$

This shows also that *a number k divides each of the numbers a, b, $\cdots$, and m only if k divides their g.c.d.*

Note 3. Relatively prime numbers. If two or more integers have 1 as their g.c.d., i.e., if they have no common divisors other than 1, they are called *relatively prime.*

For example, *if p and q are distinct primes, then p^r and q^s are relatively prime for all pairs r, s of integers.*

The following two theorems were used in the solution:

(i) *If a, b, $\cdots$, m are integers, not all zero, and if d is their g.c.d., then the integers*

$$a' = \frac{a}{d}, \quad b' = \frac{b}{d}, \quad \cdots, \quad m' = \frac{m}{d}$$

are relatively prime.

Suppose, to the contrary, that

$$(a', \quad b', \quad \cdots, \quad m') = d', \qquad \text{with} \quad d' > 1.$$

Then

$$a = a'd, \quad b = b'd, \quad \cdots, \quad m = m'd$$

are all divisible by $d'd > d$, so that d would not be the g.c.d. of $a, b, \cdots, m$.

(ii) *If b is a non-zero integer, $(a, b) = 1$, and if the product ak of a and an integer k is divisible by b, then k is divisible by b.*

For, if k were not divisible by b, then the prime power product for $|b|$ would contain at least one prime p raised to a positive power β, while the power product for $|k|$ would contain p to a power $\alpha < \beta$ (possibly $\alpha = 0$). Since $(a, b) = 1$, p cannot divide a; therefore p has the exponent $\alpha < \beta$ in the prime power product for $|ka|$, and hence ka is not divisible by b. This contradicts the hypothesis. Therefore k is divisible by b. (If a is a prime, this theorem is identical with theorem a) in the Note to the Second Solution of 1894/1.)

The following theorem is also noteworthy:

If the integer A is divisible by a and b and if $(a, b) = 1$, then A is divisible by the product ab.

For, if A is divisible by a, there is an integer k such that $A = ak$; and by theorem (ii), since $(a, b) = 1$, $A = ak$ is divisible by b only if k is, i.e., if $k = bk'$ where k' is an integer. Hence $A = abk'$ so that ab divides A.

1902 Competition

1902/1. Prove that any quadratic expression

$$Q(x) = Ax^2 + Bx + C$$

a) can be put uniquely into the form

$$Q(x) = k\frac{x(x-1)}{1\cdot 2} + lx + m,$$

where k, l, m depend on the coefficients A, B, C, and

b) $Q(x)$ takes on integral values for every integer x if and only if k, l, m are integers.

Solution. a) Since $x^2 = x^2 - x + x = x(x-1) + x$, we may write

$$x^2 = 2\frac{x(x-1)}{2} + x$$

and substitute this expression in Q. We obtain

$$Q(x) = 2A\frac{x(x-1)}{2} + (A+B)x + C,$$

and this has the desired form

$$Q(x) = k\frac{x(x-1)}{1\cdot 2} + lx + m,$$

with

$$k = 2A, \quad l = A+B, \quad m = C.$$

b) (i) If $Q(x)$ is an integer whenever x is, then, in particular, the values $Q(0), Q(1), Q(2)$ obtained by setting $x = 0, 1, 2$ are integers. But

$Q(0) = m,$ so m is an integer,

$Q(1) = l + m,$ so $l = Q(1) - m$ is an integer,

$Q(2) = k + 2l + m,$ so $k = Q(2) - 2l - m$ is an integer.

(ii) Conversely, if k, l, m are integers, then for every integral value of x, $Q(x)$ is an integer. For, if x is an integer, then either x or $x - 1$ is an even number so that $x(x-1)/2$ is an integer; so, if k, l, m are integers, $Q(\text{integer})$ is the sum of three integers, hence itself an integer.

Note 1. Polynomials that take on integral values for integral values of the variable. The following generalization of statement a) in the problem is easy to prove by induction:

Every nth degree polynomial

$$F(x) = a_0 + a_1 x + a_2 x^2 + \cdots + a_n x^n$$

can be brought into the form

(1)
$$F(x) = b_0 + b_1 \binom{x}{1} + b_2 \binom{x}{2} + \cdots + b_n \binom{x}{n},$$

where

$$\binom{x}{1} = x, \quad \binom{x}{2} = \frac{x(x-1)}{1 \cdot 2}, \quad \binom{x}{3} = \frac{x(x-1)(x-2)}{1 \cdot 2 \cdot 3}, \quad \cdots,$$

and the coefficients b_i are uniquely determined by the coefficients a_i. Moreover, if the a_i are integers, then the b_i are integers.

PROOF. The theorem is clearly true for first degree polynomials; part a) of the solution to the problem shows that it is also true for quadratic polynomials. Now, let us assume that it is true for polynomials up to degree $k-1$, and show that it then follows for polynomials of degree k. Consider

$$P_k(x) = a_0 + a_1 x + \cdots + a_{k-1} x^{k-1} + a_k x^k$$
$$= P_{k-1}(x) + a_k x^k.$$

By multiplying out, we can verify that

$$x(x-1)(x-2)\cdots(x-k+1) = x^k + G_{k-1}(x)$$

where $G_{k-1}(x)$ is a polynomial of degree $k-1$ with integral coefficients. Thus

$$x^k = x(x-1)(x-2)\cdots(x-k+1) - G_{k-1}(x),$$

and

$$P_k(x) = P_{k-1}(x) - a_k G_{k-1}(x) + k! a_k \frac{x(x-1)(x-2)\cdots(x-k+1)}{k!}.$$

The difference of two polynomials of degree $k-1$ with integral coefficients is a polynomial of at most degree $k-1$ with integral coefficients; therefore, by the induction hypothesis, the first two terms on the right may be put into the form

$$b_0 + b_1 \binom{x}{1} + \cdots + b_{k-1} \binom{x}{k-1}.$$

But then P_k is of the desired form

$$P_k(x) = b_0 + b_1 \binom{x}{1} + \cdots + b_{k-1} \binom{x}{k-1} + b_k \binom{x}{k},$$

where $b_k = k! a_k$. Moreover, if the a_i are integers, then so are the b_i.

Statement b) of the problem is generalized by the following theorem:

The polynomial $F(x)$ takes on integral values for every integer x if and only if the coefficients $b_0, b_1, \cdots, b_n$ in (1) are integers.

PROOF. The proof follows the pattern of the proof given above for the case $n = 2$.

(i') Assume that the coefficients b_i are integers; if we can show that the expressions

$$\binom{x}{k}$$

are integers when x and k are integers, $k \geq 0$, then $F(x)$ will be a sum of products of integers, and hence an integer.

We prove that

$$\binom{x}{k} = \frac{x(x-1)(x-2)\cdots(x-k+2)(x-k+1)}{1 \cdot 2 \cdot 3 \cdots (k-1)k}$$

is an integer whenever x is as follows:

If x is a positive integer or zero, then

$$\binom{x}{k}$$

is the number of possible combinations (without repetitions) of x things, k at a time,† and hence an integer; if $x < k$, this number of combinations is 0.

If x is a negative integer, say $x = -y$, then

$$\binom{-y}{k} = \frac{-y(-y-1)\cdots(-y-k+2)(-y-k+1)}{1 \cdot 2 \cdots (k-1)k}$$

$$= (-1)^k \frac{(y+k-1)(y+k-2)\cdots(y+1)y}{1 \cdot 2 \cdots (k-1)k}$$

$$= (-1)^k \binom{y+k-1}{k}$$

Here $y + k - 1$ is a positive integer, so that

$$\binom{-y}{k} = \pm \binom{y+k-1}{k}$$

is indeed an integer.

† Cf. Note 2, b) to 1895/1, page 26.

Next, we must show that, if $F(x)$ is an integer for every integer x, then the coefficients b_i are integers.

(ii') As in the case $n = 2$, observe that $b_0 = F(0)$ is an integer,

$$F(1) = b_0 + b_1, \qquad \text{so that} \quad b_1 = F(1) - b_0 \text{ is an integer,}$$

$$F(2) = b_0 + 2b_1 + b_2, \quad \text{so that} \quad b_2 = F(2) - b_0 - 2b_1 \text{ is an integer}$$

and, in general, for any integer $r \leq n$,

$$F(r) = b_0 + rb_1 + \binom{r}{2} b_2 + \cdots + \binom{r}{r} b_r,$$

since

$$\binom{r}{k} = 0 \quad \text{for} \quad r < k;$$

but

$$\binom{r}{r} = 1,$$

so this equation can be written as

$$b_r = F(r) - b_0 - rb_1 - \cdots - \binom{r-1}{r} b_{r-1}.$$

We are given that $F(r)$ is an integer, have shown that

$$\binom{k}{r}$$

is an integer whenever k is, and have already shown that $b_0, b_1, \cdots, b_{r-1}$ are integers. Therefore, b_r is a sum of products of integers, and hence an integer. We use this argument for $r = 0, 1, 2, \cdots, n$ and so show that all b_i in (1) are integers.

Remark. Observe that in the above proof, we deduced that the b_i are integers by using only the integral values $F(0)$, $F(1)$, $\cdots$, $F(n)$. The values of $F(n + 1)$, $F(n + 2)$, $\cdots$ did not matter. But once we have integers b_i, the fact that $F(x)$ is an integer for *all* integers x can be deduced from (i'). Thus we have the theorem:

If the polynomial $F(x)$ of degree n takes on integral values for $x = 0, 1, \cdots, n$, then it takes on integral values for all integers x.

Note 2. The binomial theorem and the binomial series. The expressions

$$\binom{x}{k}$$

occur in two familiar situations for positive integers x, k: first as the number of combinations of x things, k at a time (see Note 2 to 1895/1), and second as coefficients in the binomial expansion of the expression $(a + b)^x$. To show that for a positive integral exponent x,

$$(a + b)^x$$

$$= a^x + \binom{x}{1} a^{x-1}b + \cdots + \binom{x}{k} a^{x-k}b^k + \cdots + \binom{x}{x-1} ab^{x-1} + \binom{x}{x} b^x,$$

we merely analyze what it means to multiply the expression $a + b$ by itself x times: Each term in the result will consist of a product made up of one term, either a or b, from each of the x factors; these products must therefore be of the form

$$a^{x-k}b^k, \qquad 0 \leq k \leq x.$$

For a fixed value of k, we get as many products $a^{x-k}b^k$ as there are ways of picking k b's from x factors. Hence, the coefficient of the product $a^{x-k}b^k$ is

$$\binom{x}{k},$$

the number of combinations of x things, k at a time. (It is clear that this will be equal to the number of combinations of x things, $x - k$ at a time; for, the number of ways of picking out k things from x must be the same as the number of ways of holding on to $x - k$ out of x things.) This proves the identity (1).

If we set $a = b = 1$, we obtain

$$2^n = 1 + \binom{n}{1} + \binom{n}{2} + \cdots + \binom{n}{n-1} + \binom{n}{n};$$

we arrived at the same identity in Note 2, c) to 1895/1.

When x is not a positive integer, we no longer have these simple combinatorial interpretations of

$$\binom{x}{k}.$$

However, the expressions

$$\binom{x}{k},$$

called *binomial coefficients*, still retain their significance for binomials in the following sense: If z is a number such that $-1 < z < 1$ and x any real exponent (not necessarily a positive integer), then $(1 + z)^x$ is expressible as the infinite series

$$(1 + z)^x = 1 + \binom{x}{1} z + \binom{x}{2} z^2 + \cdots + \binom{x}{k} z^k + \cdots$$

It is called the binomial series and Newton† was the first to consider it for arbitrary exponents. (The proof that this infinite series represents the value $(1 + z)^x$ belongs to the calculus.) In the special case $x = -1$, this series becomes the infinite geometric progression

$$1 - z + z^2 - z^3 + \cdots$$

whose sum, for $-1 < z < 1$, is indeed

$$(1 + z)^{-1} = \frac{1}{1 + z}.$$

1902/2. Let S be a given sphere with center O and radius r. Let P be any point outside the sphere S, and let S' be the sphere with center P and radius PO. Denote by F the area of the surface of the part of S' that lies inside S. Prove that F is independent of the particular point P chosen.

Solution. Let T be the point on S' antipodal to O; that is, let the other endpoint of the diameter through O be T. Consider a plane through O, T and a point M common to both spheres, see Figure 26; let k and k' be the great circles in which this plane cuts the spheres S and S', respectively. Then k and k' have a second point of intersection, denoted by N. The lines MN and OT intersect in a point Q.

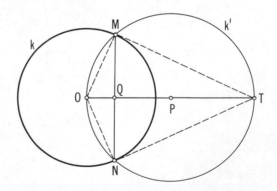

Figure 26

---

† Isaac Newton was born in 1642 and died in 1727. He was professor of mathematics at Cambridge University. He was the first to state the law of universal gravitation and, simultaneously with Leibniz, created the differential and integral calculus. He is buried in Westminster Abbey; the inscription on the marble monument that graces his tomb ends with the lines: *Sibi gratulentur mortales tale tantumque exstitisse humani generis decus.* (Mortals rejoice at so great an ornament to the human race.)

We claim that the surface area F of the spherical cap of S' inside S is equal to the product of the circumference of k' and the height OQ of the cap; i.e., that

(1) $$F = \pi \cdot OT \cdot OQ,$$

and does not depend on the position of the center P of S'.

We shall make formula (1) plausible in Note 1, below.

Note 1. On the surface area of the spherical cap, spherical segment, and sphere. a) These three surfaces are generated respectively by the following portions of a semicircle: a terminal arc, an inner arc, the entire semicircle (Figure 27a, b, c). Each surface is obtained by rotating the arc in question about the diameter of the circle. We can approximate the surface area by dividing the arc into equal segments, connecting the points of division by line segments and rotating these along with the arc; see Figure 27a', b', c'. Smaller subdivisions of the arcs give closer approximations. This is intuitively clear. What we get is the sum of the surface areas of (truncated) cones; so let us first find these areas.

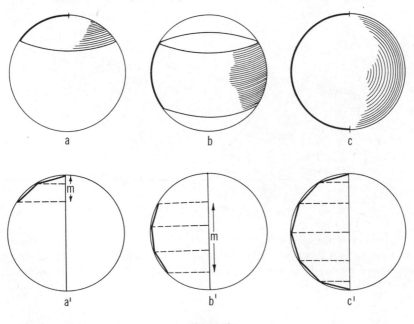

Figure 27

b) Let ρ_1 be the radius of the base of a right circular cone and d its slant height. If the cone is cut along a line from the vertex and laid out in the plane, the lateral surface is a sector of the circle of radius d, whose bounding arc has length $2\pi\rho_1$; see Figure 28. Let t_1 be the area of the sector; then, since the area of the sector is to the area $d^2\pi$ of the whole circle as the length $2\pi\rho_1$ of its arc is to the circumference $2\pi d$ of the whole circle, we have

$$\frac{t_1}{d^2\pi} = \frac{2\pi\rho_1}{2\pi d} = \frac{\rho_1}{d}.$$

This gives

$$t_1 = \pi\rho_1 d$$

as the lateral surface area of the cone.

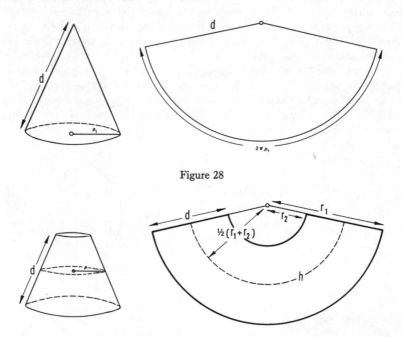

Figure 28

Figure 29

To calculate the lateral surface area of a truncated cone, the plane figure we consider is a sector of a ring, i.e. the region bounded by two concentric circles and two radii. If r_1 and r_2 stand for the radii of the concentric circles, the area of the ring is

$$r_1^2\pi - r_2^2\pi = \pi(r_1 + r_2)(r_1 - r_2),$$

where $r_1 - r_2 = d$ is the width of the ring (see Figure 29). The number $r_1 + r_2$ may be interpreted as double the radius r of the "central circle" of the ring (or double the average of r_1 and r_2). Thus the area of the ring is $2\pi rd$, that is, the product of the circumference of the central circle and the width of the ring. The area t_2 of a sector of the ring is to the area of the whole ring as the arc h of the central circle of the sector is to the length of the whole circumference of the central circle; thus we have

$$\frac{t_2}{2\pi rd} = \frac{h}{2\pi r}, \quad \text{and hence} \quad t_2 = hd.$$

The truncated cone has slant height d, and a circle of circumference h at slant distance $d/2$ from the base; see Figure 29. Designating the radius of this middle circle by ρ and the lateral surface by t, we have

(1) $t = 2\pi\rho d.$

If we take

$$\rho = \frac{\rho_1}{2}$$

(which is the radius of the circle about a cone at distance $d/2$ from the base), this expresses once more the area of the cone derived in part a).

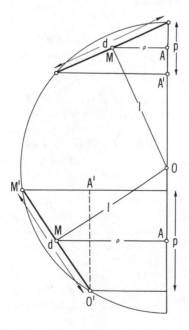

Figure 30

c) Let us return to the sphere. Let d be the length of one segment in the polygonal line approximating a great circle (see Figure 30). Let ρ be the distance from the center of this line segment to the diameter of the sphere and let l be the distance from the same point to the center of the sphere;

finally let p be the length of the projection of the line segment d on the diameter. Then the area of the surface of revolution of the segment is given by (1).

The right triangles OMA and $O'M'A'$ (see Figure 30) are similar since corresponding sides are pairwise perpendicular. Hence

$$\frac{\rho}{l} = \frac{p}{d}, \quad \text{i.e.} \quad \rho d = pl;$$

and so

$$t = 2\pi pl.$$

In words: *If we rotate a chord of a circle about a diameter it does not intersect, the surface generated has area 2π times the distance of the chord to the center of the circle times the projection of the chord on the diameter.* If we inscribe a polygonal line in an arc of a circle, every chord of length d has equal distance from the center, while the sum of the projections of the chords on the diameter equals the height m of the surface of revolution. (In case the semicircle is rotated, m is the length of the diameter.) Thus the area of the surface generated by the polygonal line is

$$2\pi lm.$$

As the subdivision is refined, l approaches the length of the radius R of the sphere. Hence the surface area of spherical cap and spherical segment is

$$2\pi Rm,$$

where R is the radius of the sphere, m the height of the surface in question. For the whole sphere, $m = 2R$, so the sphere has area $4\pi R^2$.

Note 2. The geometry of Bolyai. The theorem just proved plays a considerable role in the geometry of János Bolyai, a system of geometry independent of the parallel axiom. Let us glance at the investigations of Bolyai.

a) *The parallel axiom.* The history of the problem of parallel lines begins with Euclid's *Elements*, which takes its departure from the definitions of some basic concepts, a few broad mathematical axioms, and, what is more important, five postulates. These basic assumptions form the foundation of Euclidean geometry. We shall now consider only the fifth postulate: *If (in the plane) two lines are cut by a transversal L so that on one side of L the interior angles add up to less than two right angles, then the two lines intersect on that side of L.* This is called "the parallel postulate" because it is the basis of the theory of parallel lines.

Euclid calls two lines parallel if they are in the same plane but do not intersect, no matter how far they are extended in either direction. He proves, without using his fifth postulate, that if two lines in the plane are cut by a transversal L so that the sum of the interior angles is two right angles, then these lines are parallel (in the sense just stated). It follows that, for any line l and through any point A not on l, there exists at least one line parallel to l.

Euclid also proves that there is only one parallel to l through A, but this proof is based on his fifth postulate; in fact, the parallel postulate was designed for this purpose. While the other building blocks of Euclid's geometry are simple and straightforward, the fifth postulate sounds artificial and as if invented as an expedient. This is why the Greeks already tried to deduce it from the other, accepted, basic tenets of geometry.

b) *János Bolyai.* In the subsequent twenty-two centuries, many a brilliant mind labored on the problem, none with greater zeal than Farkas Bolyai (János's father).

Farkas Bolyai was born in Hungary in 1775 and died in 1856. He studied at Nagy-Enyed and Kolozsvár, became a friend of Baron Simon Kemény, and then went to the German universities of Jena and Göttingen (1796–1799) where he befriended Gauss, then a student there. F. Bolyai and Gauss corresponded (except for a long gap from 1816 to 1831) until Gauss' death.† Only János Bolyai's work revealed why his father was unable to prove the fifth postulate.

János Bolyai (1802–1860) was very young when he first heard of the importance of deriving the fifth postulate from the other postulates. He tried to show its dependence on the others by denying the truth of the fifth postulate and then searching for a contradiction. First, he worked in the plane. Only when he turned his attention to three-dimensional space did it dawn upon him that no such contradiction need exist—that the fifth postulate need not be a consequence of the others. Thus he was led to build a geometry in which the fifth postulate is false while all the others remain true, and found his system to be free of contradictions. From a logical point of view, this was all that mattered.

The most beautiful discoveries of János Bolyai date back to 1823, but his finished paper appeared only in 1832. Bolyai's father sent this work of 28 pages to Gauss who, on March 3, sent the saddening reply that he (Gauss) had already obtained these results, but had withheld them for fear of an uproar. This and the later news that the Russian mathematician Lobachevsky‡ had made the same discovery was a great blow to the young scientist. His father's advice, in 1825, to publish at once, proved to be sound. But Gauss' judgment was also correct; for the work of both Bolyai and Lobachevsky remained unreadable in their time. Yet their bold ideas were vindicated; today, the geometry of Bolyai-Lobachevsky is esteemed as one of the greatest accomplishments of the mind of man.

† *The Correspondence of Karl Friedrich Gauss and Farkas Bolyai,* ed. by F. Schmidt and P. Staeckel, Magyar Tud. Akademia.

‡ N. I. Lobachevsky (1793–1856) was professor in Kazan. He published his geometrical work in various forms; the shortest one is a booklet published in Berlin in 1840. The Bolyais saw only this one (via Gauss, in 1848).

It has since been recognized not only that one may construct still a different geometry by using the other negation of the fifth postulate (i.e. by assuming that there exists no line parallel to a given line l through a point outside l), but that yet other geometries, free of contradictions, can be constructed by dropping other postulates.

Which of the many geometries corresponds to reality? This is not a mathematical problem. The investigation of real space (and time) is an interesting and knotty problem in the realm of the *natural sciences*. Whatever the answer may be, the fact remains that the problem could not even have been posed as long as the human mind could not think of spaces other than the Euclidean space.

1902/3. The area T and an angle γ of a triangle are given. Determine the lengths of the sides a and b so that the side c, opposite the angle γ, is as short as possible.

First Solution. The law of cosines gives

$$c^2 = a^2 + b^2 - 2ab \cos \gamma$$

$$= (a - b)^2 + 2ab(1 - \cos \gamma).$$

We also know that

$$T = \tfrac{1}{2}ab \sin \gamma,$$

or

$$2ab = \frac{4T}{\sin \gamma};$$

hence,

$$c^2 = (a - b)^2 + 4T \frac{1 - \cos \gamma}{\sin \gamma} = (a - b)^2 + 4T \tan \frac{\gamma}{2}.$$

Since T and γ are fixed, the second term on the right is a constant. The first term is zero when $a = b$ and positive otherwise. Therefore c^2, and hence c, is a minimum when the triangle is isosceles, that is, when $a = b$. In this case,

$$2ab = 2a^2 = \frac{4T}{\sin \gamma},$$

and

$$a = b = \sqrt{\frac{2T}{\sin \gamma}}.$$

Second Solution. We shall show geometrically that c is shortest when the triangle is isosceles $(a = b)$. Let A_0B_0C be an isosceles triangle with area T and angle γ; see Figure 31. Let A_1B_1C be a second triangle with the same area, with $\angle A_1CB_1$ equal to γ, and with side CA_1 longer than side CB_1. Since the small triangles $A_0A_1B_1$ and $A_0B_0B_1$ have equal areas and the side A_0B_1 in common, they have equal altitudes; that is, $A_0A_1B_0B_1$ is a trapezoid. Moreover, $\angle A_0A_1B_0 < \angle B_1B_0A_1$ because

$$\angle A_0A_1B_0 < \angle CA_0B_0 = \angle B_1B_0A_0 < \angle B_1B_0A_1.$$

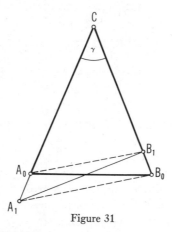

Figure 31

To show that $A_0B_0 < A_1B_1$, it now suffices to prove the following

LEMMA. *Let g be one of the parallel sides of a non-isosceles trapezoid. Then the longer diagonal goes through that end point of g at which the inner angle is smaller.*

PROOF: In the trapezoid $PQRS$ (see Figure 32), let PQ and RS be parallel and assume that

$$\angle SPQ > \angle PQR.$$

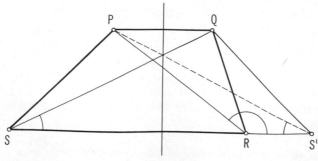

Figure 32

Let $PQS'S$ be symmetric with respect to the perpendicular bisector of PQ ; then S' is on the line through S and R and beyond R , and $\angle RS'P = \angle QSR$. Since $\angle PRS'$ is an exterior angle of $\triangle SPR$,

$$\angle PRS' > \angle PSR, \quad \text{and} \quad \angle PSR = \angle PSQ + \angle QSR.$$

Hence

$$\angle PRS' > \angle QSR = \angle RS'P.$$

Since, in a triangle, the longer side lies opposite the larger angle, it follows that in $\triangle PRS'$

$$PS' > PR.$$

Since $PS' = QS$ by symmetry, we have proved that

$$QS > PR.$$

This establishes the lemma. When applied to the trapezoid $A_0A_1B_0B_1$, it establishes the fact that the side $A_0B_0=c$ belonging to an isosceles triangle is shortest.

Third Solution. Consider all triangles with a given area T and a common angle γ at the vertex C . If one of these has a shorter base c than the others, shrink† all the others until their bases also have lengths c . The resulting figures will have areas smaller than T . We have transformed our problem into that of finding, among all triangles with a given base c and a given vertex angle γ , the one with the largest area.

The vertices C of all such triangles lie on an arc of a circle with radius $c/2 \sin \gamma$ and chord c (see Note to 1895/2, First Solution). The triangle with the longest altitude to c will have the greatest area; but the altitude to c is longest when it is erected at the midpoint of the chord c , so the solution is an isosceles triangle.

It follows that, among all triangles of area T and angle γ at C , the side opposite C is shortest for the isosceles triangle.

1903 Competition

1903/1. Let $n = 2^{p-1}(2^p - 1)$, and let $2^p - 1$ be a prime number. Prove that the sum of all positive divisors of n (not including n itself) is exactly n .

---

† "Shrinking" a plane figure means to decrease its size while its shape is retained; i.e., at each stage of shrinking, the figure is similar to the original.

Solution. If we set $q = 2^p - 1$, $n = 2^{p-1}q$, the divisors of n are (cf. 1901/3, Note 1):

$$1, \quad 2, \quad 2^2, \quad \cdots, \quad 2^{p-2}, \quad 2^{p-1},$$

$$q, \quad 2q, \quad 2^2q, \quad \cdots, \quad 2^{p-2}q.$$

We sum the first geometric progression:

$$1 + 2 + 2^2 + \cdots + 2^{p-2} + 2^{p-1} = \frac{2^p - 1}{2 - 1} = 2^p - 1 = q;$$

the sum of the other geometric series is

$$q(2^{p-1} - 1) = 2^{p-1}q - q = n - q.$$

Therefore, the desired sum is

$$q + n - q = n.$$

Note. Perfect numbers. A positive number n is called a *perfect number* if the sum of all its positive divisors less than n is exactly n. Perfect numbers were treated already in Euclid (*Elements*, IX, no. 36). The smallest perfect number is

$$2(2^2 - 1) = 6 = 1 + 2 + 3.$$

Our theorem yields only *even* perfect numbers. Deeper analysis reveals that it yields *every even* perfect number.† The questions:

(a) Are there infinitely many *even* perfect numbers?
(b) Are there any *odd* perfect numbers at all?
are still unanswered.

1903/2. For a given pair of values x and y satisfying $x = \sin \alpha$, $y = \sin \beta$, there can be four different values of $z = \sin (\alpha + \beta)$.

a) Set up a relation between x, y and z not involving trigonometric functions or radicals.

b) Find those pairs of values (x, y) for which $z = \sin (\alpha + \beta)$ takes on fewer than four distinct values.

Solution. a) If $\sin \alpha = x$, $\sin \beta = y$, then

$$\cos \alpha = \pm\sqrt{1 - x^2}, \quad \cos \beta = \pm\sqrt{1 - y^2},$$

---

† As of April 1962, only 20 of Euclid's perfect numbers have been computed. The first 18 may be found in *Recreational Mathematics*, August 1961, pp. 56–59, and the 19th and 20th appear in the April 1962 issue of the same magazine, pp. 29–31.

and
$$z = \sin(\alpha + \beta) = \sin \alpha \cos \beta + \cos \alpha \sin \beta$$

may take on the following four values:

$$z_1 = x\sqrt{1 - y^2} + y\sqrt{1 - x^2},$$
$$-z_1 = -x\sqrt{1 - y^2} - y\sqrt{1 - x^2},$$

(1)

$$z_2 = x\sqrt{1 - y^2} - y\sqrt{1 - x^2},$$
$$-z_2 = -x\sqrt{1 - y^2} + y\sqrt{1 - x^2}.$$

The equation having these values as roots is

$$(z - z_1)(z + z_1)(z - z_2)(z + z_2) = 0,$$

or

(2) $\qquad (z^2 - z_1^2)(z^2 - z_2^2) = z^4 - (z_1^2 + z_2^2)z^2 + z_1^2 z_2^2 = 0,$

where

$$z_1^2 + z_2^2 = 2[x^2(1 - y^2) + y^2(1 - x^2)] = 2(x^2 - 2x^2y^2 + y^2)$$

and

$$z_1 z_2 = x^2(1 - y^2) - y^2(1 - x^2) = x^2 - y^2.$$

If we substitute these values in (2) we obtain the relation

(3) $\qquad z^4 - 2(x^2 - 2x^2y^2 + y^2)z^2 + (x^2 - y^2)^2 = 0$

between x, y and z, and this expression is free of trigonometric functions and radicals.

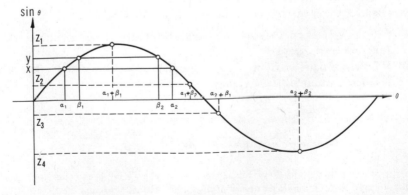

Figure 33

b) In general, eq. (3) has the four distinct roots given in (1). [The graph of the sine function in Fig. 33 illustrates how each value of x between -1 and 1 leads to two angles α between 0 and π such that $\alpha = \arcsin x$, and similarly for y and β, and how different values of $z = \sin(\alpha + \beta)$ result, depending on which α we combine with β.] Equations (1) tell us that we obtain fewer than four distinct roots in the following cases:

1. $z_1 = z_2$, or $z_1 = -z_2$, which arise if

$$y\sqrt{1 - x^2} = 0 \quad \text{or} \quad x\sqrt{1 - y^2} = 0,$$

that is, if $y = 0$, or $x^2 = 1$, or if $x = 0$, or $y^2 = 1$; in other words, if either x or y takes on any one of the values, 0, 1, or -1.

2. $z_1 = -z_1$, or $z_2 = -z_2$, which arise if

$$x\sqrt{1 - y^2} = -y\sqrt{1 - x^2} \quad \text{or} \quad x\sqrt{1 - y^2} = y\sqrt{1 - x^2},$$

that is, if $x^2(1 - y^2) = y^2(1 - x^2)$ or, equivalently, if

$$x^2 = y^2 \quad \text{or} \quad x = \pm y.$$

1903/3. Let A, B, C, D be the vertices of a rhombus; let k_1 be the circle through B, C, and D; let k_2 be the circle through A, C, and D; let k_3 be the circle through A, B, and D; and let k_4 be the circle through A, B, and C. Prove that the tangents to k_1 and k_3 at B form the same angle as the tangents to k_2 and k_4 at A.

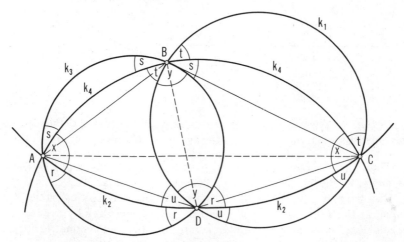

Figure 34

Solution. The theorem is true for any quadrilateral $ABCD$. (Figure 34 shows a convex quadrilateral and Figure 35 shows a non-convex quadrilateral. The proof we present below holds for all.)

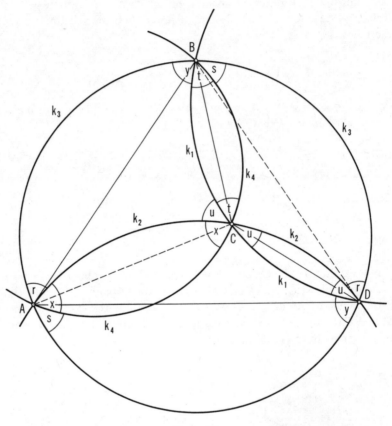

Figure 35

Definition. The angle between two intersecting curves is defined to be the angle between the tangents to the curves at their point of intersection.

Thus, the theorem to be proved may be phrased: The angle between k_1 and k_3 at B is equal to the angle between k_2 and k_4 at A.

Observe first that the angles between any two intersecting circles are equal at both intersections. To see this, join the centers by a line; the whole figure is symmetric with respect to this line and symmetric angles are equal. It follows that the angles marked by the same letters in Figure 34 are equal. The same is true for Figure 35.

Moreover, in each case,

$$r + x + s = 180° \quad \text{at } A; \quad s + y + t = 180° \quad \text{at } B;$$
$$t + x + u = 180° \quad \text{at } C; \quad u + y + r = 180° \quad \text{at } D.$$

Therefore

$$(r + x + s) - (s + y + t) + (t + x + u) - (u + y + r) = 0,$$

or

$$2(x - y) = 0.$$

Hence, $x = y$, as we set out to prove.

1904 Competition

1904/1. Prove that, if a pentagon (five-sided polygon) inscribed in a circle has equal angles, then its sides are equal.

Solution. In the pentagon $A_0A_1A_2A_3A_4$ of Figure 36, the vertices A_0, A_1, A_2 and A_3, A_2, A_1 determine congruent triangles because:

1. $A_1A_2 = A_2A_1$,

2. $\sphericalangle A_0A_1A_2 = \sphericalangle A_3A_2A_1$ by assumption, and

3. $\sphericalangle A_1A_0A_2 = \sphericalangle A_2A_3A_1$, because they are inscribed angles subtending the same arc.

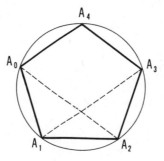

Figure 36

It follows from the congruence of these triangles that

$$A_0A_1 = A_2A_3.$$

Similarly, by using other pairs of congruent triangles, it can be shown that $$A_0A_1 = A_2A_3 = A_4A_0 = A_1A_2 = A_3A_4.$$

This theorem is true for polygons with an odd number $(2n + 1)$ of sides, and the same proof applies. For polygons with an even number $(2n)$ of sides, the theorem is false; the simplest counter example is an inscribed rectangle.

1904/2. If a is a natural number, show that the number of positive integral solutions of the indeterminate equation

$$(1) \qquad x_1 + 2x_2 + 3x_3 + \cdots + nx_n = a$$

is equal to the number of non-negative integral solutions of

$$(2) \qquad y_1 + 2y_2 + 3y_3 + \cdots + ny_n = a - \frac{n(n + 1)}{2}.$$

[By a *solution* of equation (1), we mean a set of numbers $\{x_1, x_2, \cdots, x_n\}$ which satisfies equation (1).]

Solution. The set $\{x_1, x_2, \cdots, x_n\}$ satisfies equation (1) if and only if the set

$$\{y_1 = x_1 - 1, \quad y_2 = x_2 - 1, \quad \cdots, \quad y_n = x_n - 1\}$$

satisfies the equation

$$(3) \quad (y_1 + 1) + 2(y_2 + 1) + 3(y_3 + 1) + \cdots + n(y_n + 1) = a,$$

obtained from (1) by substituting $y_i + 1$ for x_i $(i = 1, 2, \cdots, n)$. Equation (3) is equivalent to

$$y_1 + 2y_2 + \cdots + ny_n = a - (1 + 2 + \cdots + n)$$

$$= a - \frac{n(n + 1)}{2}.$$

Moreover, the x's are positive integers if and only if the y's are non-negative integers.

Thus, for every set of values $\{x_1, x_2, \cdots, x_n\}$, there is exactly one set of values $\{y_1, y_2, \cdots, y_n\}$. Hence, (1) and (2) have the same number of solutions of the specified types.

1904/3. Let A_1A_2 and B_1B_2 be the diagonals of a rectangle, and let O be its center. Find and construct the set of all points P that satisfy simultaneously the four inequalities

$$A_1P > OP, \quad A_2P > OP, \quad B_1P > OP, \quad B_2P > OP.$$

Solution. Let P be any point in the plane and let P' be its projection on the line through A_1 and A_2; see Fig. 37. Then A_1P is greater than, equal to, less than OP according as A_1P' is greater than, equal to, less than OP'. Hence the locus of points satisfying $A_1P > OP$ is the half plane containing O and bounded by the perpendicular bisector of the segment A_1O. Similarly, the locus of points P satisfying $A_2P > OP$ is the half plane containing O and bounded by the perpendicular bisector of A_2O; the locus of points P satisfying, respectively, $B_1P > OP$ and $B_2P > OP$ consists of the half planes containing O and bounded by the perpendicular bisectors of B_1O and B_2O.

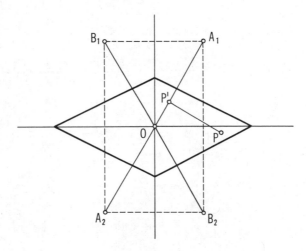

Figure 37

The locus of points satisfying all four inequalities simultaneously is the common part of all these loci, i.e., the interior of the parallelogram formed by the perpendicular bisectors of the segments A_1O, A_2O, B_1O, B_2O. This parallelogram is always a rhombus because its diagonals bisect the angles at which A_1A_2 and B_1B_2 intersect, and hence are perpendicular.

1905 Competition

1905/1. For given positive integers n and p, find necessary and sufficient conditions for the system of equations

$$x + py = n, \qquad x + y = p^z$$

to have a solution (x, y, z) of positive integers. Prove also that there is at most one such solution.

Solution. We observe first that the second equation cannot be satisfied by the positive integers x, y, z unless $p > 1$, that is $p - 1 > 0$.

Next, we solve the second equation for y and substitute its value in the first equation, so that

$$x + py = x + p(p^z - x) = x - px + p^{z+1} = x(1 - p) + p^{z+1} = n$$

or, since $p - 1 \neq 0$,

$$(1) \qquad x = \frac{p^{z+1} - n}{p - 1} = \frac{p^{z+1} - 1}{p - 1} - \frac{n - 1}{p - 1}.$$

From the second given equation, we find

$$y = p^z - x = p^z - \frac{p^{z+1} - n}{p - 1} = \frac{p^{z+1} - p^z - p^{z+1} + n}{p - 1},$$

that is

$$(2) \qquad y = \frac{n - p^z}{p - 1} = \frac{n - 1}{p - 1} - \frac{p^z - 1}{p - 1}.$$

Since, for every positive integer z,

$$\frac{p^{z+1} - 1}{p - 1} = p^z + p^{z-1} + \cdots + 1$$

and

$$\frac{p^z - 1}{p - 1} = p^{z-1} + p^{z-2} + \cdots + 1$$

are integers, relations (1) and (2) tell us that x and y are integers if and only if $n - 1$ is a multiple of $p - 1$. Moreover, x is positive if and only if

$$p^{z+1} > n,$$

and y is positive if and only if

$$n > p^z;$$

thus x and y are positive if and only if

$$(3) \qquad p^{z+1} > n > p^z,$$

so that n must be a number between two consecutive powers of p, z being the value of the smaller exponent. We summarize the necessary and sufficient conditions for the given system to have a solution in positive integers:

(a) $p > 1$,

(b) $n - 1$ is a multiple of $p - 1$ (and hence $n \geq p$),

(c) n is not an integral power of p.

If these conditions are satisfied, then the inequalities (3) determine z uniquely and once the value of z is determined, eqs. (1) and (2) determine x and y uniquely. Therefore, if (a), (b), (c) are satisfied, there is a unique solution (x, y, z).

1905/2. Divide the unit square into 9 equal squares by means of two pairs of lines parallel to the sides; see Figure 38. Now remove the central square. Treat the remaining 8 squares the same way, and repeat the process n times.

a) How many squares of side length $1/3^n$ remain?

b) What is the sum of the areas of the removed squares as n becomes infinite?

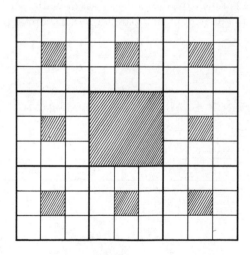

Figure 38

Solution. a) After the first step 8 squares are left, each with side length $\frac{1}{3}$. After two steps

$$8 \cdot 9 - 8 = 8(9 - 1) = 8^2$$

squares are left, each with side length $1/3^2$. After three steps

$$8^2 \cdot 9 - 8^2 = 8^2(9 - 1) = 8^3$$

squares are left, each with side length $1/3^3$. After n steps, 8^n squares are left and each has side length $1/3^n$.

b) The sum of the areas of the squares that are left is

$$8^n \left(\frac{1}{3^n}\right)^2 = \left(\frac{8}{9}\right)^n ;$$

therefore, the sum of the areas of the removed squares is

$$1 - \left(\frac{8}{9}\right)^n .$$

As n increases, $(8/9)^n$ becomes smaller and smaller and approaches 0 since $8/9$ is less than 1. Therefore, the sum of the areas of the removed squares approaches 1 as n approaches infinity.

1905/3. Let C_1 be any point on side AB of a triangle ABC (see Figure 39), and draw C_1C. Let A_1 be the intersection of BC extended and the line through A parallel to CC_1; similarly let B_1 be the intersection of AC extended and the line through B parallel to CC_1. Prove that

$$\frac{1}{AA_1} + \frac{1}{BB_1} = \frac{1}{CC_1} .$$

Solution. Since AA_1, BB_1, CC_1 are parallel, $\triangle CAC_1 \sim \triangle B_1AB$ and $\triangle CBC_1 \sim \triangle A_1BA$. It follows that

$$\frac{CC_1}{B_1B} = \frac{AC_1}{AB} , \quad \text{and} \quad \frac{CC_1}{A_1A} = \frac{C_1B}{AB} .$$

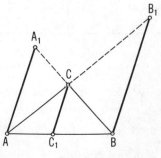

Figure 39

Adding these relations, we find that

$$\frac{CC_1}{B_1B} + \frac{CC_1}{A_1A} = \frac{AC_1 + C_1B}{AB} = \frac{AB}{AB} = 1,$$

and dividing by CC_1, we obtain the desired result†

† If a and b are two positive numbers, then the number c, defined by

$$\frac{1}{a} + \frac{1}{b} = \frac{2}{c}$$

(i.e. the number whose reciprocal is the average of the reciprocals of the given numbers), is called the *harmonic mean* of a and b.

The theorem just proved shows that, if a and b are lengths of parallel sides of a trapezoid, then their harmonic mean is the length of the segment through the intersection of the diagonals and parallel to the parallel sides.

$$\frac{1}{AA_1} + \frac{1}{BB_1} = \frac{1}{CC_1}.$$

Classification† of Problems

Number theory:	1894/1, 1896/1, 1898/1, 1899/3, 1900/1, 1901/1, 1901/3, 1902/1, 1903/1.
Combinatorics:	1895/1.
Quadratic equations:	1896/2, 1899/2.
Quadratic functions:	1902/1.
Equations of higher degree:	1903/2.
Diophantine equations:	1894/1, 1904/2, 1905/1.
Number sequences:	1905/1, 1905/2.
Inequalities:	1896/1.

Plane geometry (without trigonometry)

Proofs:	1903/3, 1904/1, 1905/3.
Computations:	1894/3.
Loci:	1895/2, 1904/3.
Constructions:	1894/2, 1895/2, 1896/3, 1897/3, 1898/3, 1900/2.
Extreme values:	1902/3.
Inequalities:	1897/2, 1904/3.

† Since the problems and specially their solutions often involve several mathematical disciplines, this classification is necessarily arbitrary and somewhat incomplete.

Angle measurement: 1899/1, 1901/2, 1903/2.

Trigonometry: 1894/3, 1895/3, 1896/3,
                                  1897/1, 1897/2, 1898/2,
                                  1899/1.

Solid geometry: 1902/2.

From physics: 1900/3.

List of Explanatory Notes

List of Biographical Notes

List of Winners

1894	Mihály Seidner	Pál Pap
1895	Emil Riesz	Ignác Pilczer
1896	Aladár Visnya	Győző Zemplén
1897	Bernát Fazekas	Lipót Fejér
1898	Tivadar Kármán	Gábor Gróffits
1899	Ödön Kornis	Ödön Spiczer
1900	Iréneusz Juvantz	Kázmér Szmodics
1901	Gyula Póka	Ernő Baranyó
1902	Dénes Kőnig	Hildegárd Szmodics
1903	Alfréd Haar	Béla Horvay
1904	Marcel Riesz	István Fuchs
1905	Gyula Ujj	Constantin Neubauer